HEDGES
SHELTERBELTS
AND SCREENS

HEDGES
SHELTERBELTS
AND SCREENS

BY

A. D. C. LE SUEUR

COUNTRY LIFE LIMITED

2-10 TAVISTOCK STREET COVENT GARDEN

LONDON W.C.2

First published in 1951
by Country Life Limited
Tavistock Street London W.C.2
Printed in Great Britain by
Morrison and Gibb Ltd
Tanfield Edinburgh

CONTENTS

ILLUSTRATIONS

FOREWORD

I WISH to express my gratitude for assistance to the following: Mr. A. H. Popert; Mr. R. W. B. Newton; Mr. G. H. W. Cruttwell; Mr. A. Bates, Head Gardener at Dropmore, Bucks; and Mr. W. H. Ward. B.Sc., A.M.I.C.E.

I would also like to thank the following for the loan of photographs: Messrs. A. Guinness, Son and Co. (hedges and screens at Park Royal); The Viscount Iveagh (Windbreak at Elveden); Mr. H. Hewlett, F.R.I.C.S. (Damage caused by Poplar Roots); Mr. R. W. B. Newton (Laying of Thorn Fences); *The Isle of Ely and Wisbech Advertiser* (Fenblow).

Thanks are also due to the United States Department of Agriculture, for permission to make use of Bulletin No. 1405 (The Windbreak as a Farm Asset) and to the Controller of H.M. Stationery Office for permission to publish the photograph of windbreaks from the air.

I owe much to my wife, Winifred Le Sueur, for without her assistance and advice this book would never have been completed.

Finally I wish to say that the omission of any reference to the comparatively new method of hedge cutting by machinery is intentional. Whilst its value from the labour point of view is obvious, its effect, as far as the life and well-being of the hedge itself is concerned, remains to be seen.

Farnham Common, Bucks   A. D. C. LE SUEUR

CHAPTER I

CONCERNING HEDGES

THE English hedge is a part of English history. It has been an important factor in the making of English gardens, and has played a leading part in the making of the English landscape. From a utilitarian point of view its value has been even greater, for without fences (which for many generations were hedges) the old breeders could never have built up English livestock to make it what it is today, the finest in the world.

The garden hedge of the Middle Ages was really a fence, as it was almost invariably made of wattle. Contemporary illustrations dealing with medieval horticulture frequently portray a very large lady and a very small tree in a garden surrounded by a woven fence of wood, the pattern of which is exactly the same as that of the hazel hurdles so often used today for exactly the same purpose. As civilization progressed wattling gradually gave place to more open fencing, below which flowers or shrubs were planted and encouraged to climb over palings and posts. At that time the most popular hedge plants appear to have been whitethorn and sweetbrier. By the beginning of the sixteenth century posts and palings were less fashionable, and the live hedge was developing into the type that is known today.

Formally clipped hedges appear to have come in with the Tudors. Hill[1], writing in 1608, refers at length to the thorn hedge 'artely laid', stating that in a few years 'it waxeth so thicke and strong that hardly any person can enter into the ground saving by the garden door'. He also mentions privet, which is given strength by clipping. Other plants used for the purpose were sweetbrier, cypress, hornbeam, box, yew and holly. John Evelyn, writing in 1658 says of yew: 'I do again name them for hedges, preferably for beauty and a stiff defence to any plant I have seen, and may on that account without vanity be said to have been the first which brought it into fashion, as well for defence as for a

[1] *The Gardener's Labyrinth.*

succedaneum to cypress whether in hedges or pyramids'. The cypress referred to must be the Mediterranean type (*C. semper-virens*). It is interesting to note that this tree, once apparently largely used for ornamental purposes, is now comparatively rare, even in the warmer parts of the country. While this is possibly due to a change in climate, its lack of stamina was always known, as Evelyn points out the superiority of yew as far as cold weather is concerned.

Evelyn speaks highly of holly as a hedge plant, 'glittering with its armed and varnished leaves'. He suggests a way of raising holly hedges which should commend itself to those who want such hedges but are afraid of the cost. He planted one holly to five whitethorn, gradually removing the thorns as the holly spread. Given time and patience there seems no reason why this idea should not be practicable, as the heavier-leafed holly would certainly kill out the light-demanding thorn.

This is the way Evelyn raised the great hedge at Sayes Court, near Deptford. This hedge was four hundred feet long, nine feet high and five feet thick. Its appearance was eventually ruined by Peter the Great, who lived at Sayes Court while studying English shipbuilding, and is said to have amused himself by being pushed through the hedge while sitting in a wheelbarrow.

Beech as a hedge plant appears to have been little used, and Evelyn ignores its value completely. It does not appear to have been much employed until the middle of the eighteenth century. It was about this time that William Kent appeared on the scene. Kent was one of the leaders of the 'natural gardening' school. He did not approve of straight lines, and ripped avenues and hedges out without mercy. He was the originator of the 'ha-ha', or sunken fence, actually a ditch dividing gardens from fields or park. Another landscape gardener, the famous 'Capability' Brown, followed Kent. While many of his ideas were different, he agreed with Kent on the subject of avenues and hedges, and in the late eighteenth century many beautiful gardens were 'improved' out of knowledge under his guidance and that of his followers.

Fortunately for hedges the work of this extremist school of landscape gardening was mainly confined to the property of the wealthy, and as garden fashion gradually swung back to what might be called a formal-natural type, and suburban residences began to increase in number, the hedge gradually re-established itself as a permanent and highly desirable garden unit.

The so-called 'garden hedge' has many uses. Apart from acting as a boundary and barrier it protects flowers and vegetables from wind and cold. It creates the privacy beloved of the average Briton. It may be used as a background for brightly flowering plants and shrubs. Carefully chosen and sited, the hedge can add much to the architectural value of a house. Not so carefully chosen or sited the result can be the reverse. And it is perfectly possible for a hedge, whether flowering or formal, to be a thing of beauty in itself.

In past times the number of species and their varieties available for hedges was comparatively small. Today choice is restricted by the fact that most nurseries have barely recovered from the war years, when thousands of plants were torn up and burnt to allow for food production.

The hedge plants mentioned in this book cover practically all those usually employed for the purpose, and some less frequently used. The book does not attempt to deal with every plant that might be used, or even every plant that ever has been used. Wyman[1] mentions nearly 150 species and their varieties considered suitable for making hedges in the United States. Truly, as the prophet might have said: 'Of making many hedges there is no end'.

Farm hedges have been in existence for many hundreds of years, but their importance as far as agriculture is concerned is not apparent until the middle of the eighteenth and early nineteenth centuries, when the Enclosure Acts were in full swing. While early writers seem to have paid little attention to farm hedges, published works of this period devoted much space to the subject.

In the early days of farming boundaries were primitive. Fields were communal and cattle were herded. Hedges were therefore considered unnecessary, and boundaries were frequently indicated by trees or stones. In Buckinghamshire, woodland was often demarcated by 'bound holes', which consisted of shallow oblong

---

[1] *Hedges, Screens and Windbreaks.* New York, 1938.

pits set about a hundred yards apart. Traces of these holes, dug many hundreds of years ago, can occasionally still be found in the beechwoods of the Chiltern Hills. The hedges of the early days were very rough, compared with modern types, and were often allowed to grow to considerable size before being cut, in order to get 'browse' for the cattle, fuel for the house and poles for fences. They were almost invariably set on banks, and while there is no doubt that thorn was used to some extent, most hedges consisted of species of greater use for fuel and fence, ash being frequent where the soil was suitable. The tall tree-covered banks of the north and south-west of England are survivals.

The expression 'quick set' for a thorn hedge, in universal use today, did not convey the same meaning in earlier times. For many generations a quick set hedge has been composed solely of thorn. But the term refers in fact to the establishment of a live (i.e. quick) hedge, and has no real connection with the actual species used.

Norden, writing in 1607, states that the best way to make a 'quick set' is to mix the seed of oak, thorn and ash together, wind them into a rough straw rope and bury the rope along the top of the bank.

The big bank hedge survived well into the nineteenth century, and inspection of prints and illustrations from books of the period dealing with sport shows that frequently they were allowed to grow to a very considerable size before being cut. A definition of the 'bullfinch', a type of fence somewhat disliked by riders to hounds, is worth quoting: 'A quick set hedge of perhaps fifty years' growth, with a ditch on one side or the other, and so high and strong that one cannot clear it'.[1]

This definition is not one that would commend itself to many living foxhunters, or to even more numerous dead ones. The derivation of the word is unknown, but by some it is considered to be based on the 'bull fences' which originated on the grazing lands of the Shires, and which had to be unusually strong in order to prevent the straying of heavy bullocks. These hedges, often a combination of hedge and fence, were allowed to grow to a considerable height before being cut back, and were frequently

[1] *Quarterly Review*, 1832.

'so big and so black that if a lanthorn 'ad been 'eld on the far side you couldn't have seen it'.[1]

It is probable, therefore, that the term 'bullfinch', as universally applied today to practically any hedge with considerable top growth, is derived from the Leicestershire 'bullfinch hedge', itself a type rather than a condition.

The planting and establishment of a bullfinch is given in detail on pages 68 and 69.

With the coming of coal and wire, and more scientific farming, the size of hedges began to decline. The need for wood fuel decreased, and as land became more valuable, hedges had to be kept to reasonable limits. So in the better class agricultural districts lower, narrower and better-kept hedges became the rule. Alken's pictures of fox-hunting almost invariably show hedges of this kind.

Planting 'on the flat' had, up to this time, been comparatively rare, although William Marshall, writing in 1785, states that planting without a bank was a common practice in the Pickering district of Yorkshire, and one that he highly approved of, considering that it was superior to bank planting in every way. In such cases the hedge was formed by excavating a trench, setting the plants on the side (which had to be vertical) and then refilling.

This opinion was also held by the early railway engineers. Practically all hedges up to the time of the coming of the railway had been banks, with a deep ditch, or sometimes two ditches, for drainage purposes. Railway fences had no bank, and not always a ditch, and proved so satisfactory from the point of view of expense as well as of growth that wherever possible agriculturists adopted them: 'bank and ditch' ceased to be the general practice on farms where new hedges were being made. A modified form known as 'ditch and hedge' is the standard method in use today. Such hedges usually possess a bank, but compared with the older type its height is negligible.

At one time good hedges indicated a good farmer, but nowadays it is hard to blame the man who finds that the present-day scale of agricultural wages does not allow him to spend money on anything except essentials. The benefits of the hedgerow are

[1] Mr Jorrocks in *Handley Cross*.

difficult to express in terms of money, and if labour is to be cut down hedging is naturally one of the first things thought of.

Hedges have certain disadvantages, although most of these are due to bad management rather than to the hedge itself. One objection is that they encourage weeds and vermin. This may apply to the big old rough hedge and bank, but certainly not to the well-kept hedge planted on the flat. Another objection is the waste of land. This can be lessened by close trimming and good laying. On a five hundred acre farm, for example, with fifty fields of about ten acres each, surrounded by hedges properly trimmed and cared for, the loss should not be equivalent to the area of one field. With rough, old neglected hedges it could be more than twice as much.

There is, of course, one very sound reason for the present reduction in the number of farm hedges, and that is mechanical cultivation. Large fields are more economical to deal with, and where combines are used are almost a necessity.

There is, however, one very cogent argument in favour of the retention and preservation of rural hedges wherever possible. From the point of view of national amenity it seems a pity that Authority, anxious to develop England as a tourist resort, does not appear fully to realize the attraction of the countryside as a drawing asset. It does not seem to grasp that a high proportion of the visitors from abroad are more interested in the trees, fields and hedges that go to make up the English landscape than in urban attractions, many of which are probably just as good, if not far better, in their own country.

The Town and Country Planning Act, it is true, devotes much space to regulations dealing with the preservation of trees, but in many parts of the country the hedgerow is, from the point of view of amenity, just as important as the tree.

CHAPTER II

ORNAMENTAL HEDGES : EVERGREEN

ORNAMENTAL hedges can be divided into three classes: evergreen, deciduous and flowering.

The evergreen hedge is particularly useful where shelter or screening is required. It also makes an excellent boundary hedge, as it creates a greater sense of privacy than the deciduous or the flowering hedge. Where the garden is formal, clipped evergreen hedges with regular outlines are almost essential. As an internal hedge in small gardens it should be avoided where possible, unless kept very low, as it tends to shorten distance and makes the area appear smaller than it is.

The deciduous hedge, losing its leaf in winter, has less value as a screen or shelter, but even when leafless such a hedge can be pleasant and light in appearance. It is generally easier to grow and keep in order than the evergreen hedge, and is fairly easy to patch up if things go wrong, which is not always the case with heavy evergreens.

Flowering hedges should be much more freely used. Although they require more skill and attention than other kinds of hedge they are far more interesting and ornamental, and brighten any garden, often making it appear larger than it really is. Owing to the method of treatment necessary they must be considered as rough or semi-formal, and in some cases, *Berberis stenophylla* for example, they need a good deal of room. There are, however, a number of species that are quite suitable for small gardens.

In this and the succeeding chapter will be found not all but a considerable number of species suitable for making hedges, with suggestions for their establishment and management.

Holly (*Ilex Aquifolium*)

Holly is a first-class garden hedge. Properly grown it makes an impenetrable barrier, and its dark shining leaves form an excellent background for brightly coloured plants and shrubs. It grows almost anywhere, except in wet clays, and does particularly well in peaty, light soils.

Holly is propagated by seed. After the berries are collected they are mixed with twice their bulk of sand, and left in a heap in the open for the flesh to rot. The mixture of seed and sand is then sown in a well-dug bed. After two years the seedlings are transplanted for another two years, and then every two years until they are the size required. When transplanting is done long roots should always be shortened.

The site of a holly hedge should be well dug, preferably trenched and broken up to a depth of 2 feet at least. Planting can be done in autumn or late spring. May is generally considered best. If the plants have been moved with naked roots instead of the more usual ball of earth they should be pruned back to two-thirds of the original height. Well-rotted manure can be used with advantage, but it should be put in well below the root system.

The size of the plants depends on requirements, and incidentally on the amount of money available. Trees up to 5 feet can be moved safely, but perhaps the ideal size is about 24 inches. Such plants should be spaced 18 inches apart.

If newly-planted trees lose their leaves there is no cause for alarm. If, however, the leaves turn brown and hang on the tree the hedge should be cut back, and plenty of water given to both roots and leaves.

Hedges must be clipped annually. April is preferred by some people, as the new young growth hides the cuts. On the other hand if they are clipped in August or September a short growth put on helps to ripen the young stems, and reduces damage by frost.

The height to which the hedge is allowed to grow is a matter of taste and time. One can get equally good hedges 5 feet and 20 feet high. As regards shape, small hedges are usually square-sided and flat-topped. Tall ones should be clipped back at an angle, so that the top is flat and about a foot wide. This will prevent damage from snow.

Old, neglected hedges with thin bottoms can often be much improved by cutting hard back, and putting composted soil or well-rotted manure above the roots.

1. Hedges at Park Royal Brewery, London. In the foreground: *Berberis stenophylla*; on either side of the road: thorn, formal and informal; on the edge of the railway cutting: myrobalan plum.

2. *A sixteen-year-old willow screen, forty feet high, at Park Royal Brewery, London.*

3. *The same screen from the ground, showing its efficient and rapid blocking effect.*

18

Holly is slow growing, and may take ten years to make a hedge 6 feet high.

Yew (*Taxus baccata*)

Yew is a first-class hedge plant. It is generally classed as a slow-growing type, but if properly looked after it does not take long to obtain a satisfactory result.

Yew is propagated from seed in the same way as holly. It is not particular as to soil, and is especially useful for chalky situations. It stands side shade, and to some extent smoke, so that it can be used for town and suburban planting.

Hedge plants should be set at from 18 inches to 2 feet apart, in October or May. When pruning for shape it is best to cut back the top very lightly until the height required is reached. The sides should be kept well clipped, in order to obtain dense growth, if necessary doing this clipping twice a year, preferably in May or June and again in August. With mature hedges one clipping is generally enough, and that should be done in August or early September.

Yew is, as a rule, clipped with a flat top. This is generally satisfactory, but it is desirable to have a slight slope inwards from ground-level to top.

Old hedges can be improved by adding new soil and well-rotted manure. Gaps can sometimes be filled by bringing branches into them and wiring them in place. Gaps at ground-level can sometimes be filled by putting in young plants, but this is not always successful owing to shading or drip from the older trees and excessive root competition. Young plants used for this purpose need to be very well rooted, and very carefully planted, and to be given time to establish themselves before any pruning to shape is attempted.

Young hedges need water in dry weather. In this connection two heavy waterings per week are far more valuable than six light ones. A light mulch of leaf mould helps to conserve the water.

The use of artificial manures, apart from bone meal, is not recommended, but according to the late Vicary Gibbs a small handful of nitrate of soda applied to each plant in spring will improve growth to a considerable degree.

B

Yew for hedging (1950) 12 to 18 inches high costs about £25 per 100. When buying care should be taken to obtain plants branched down to the ground. The sacking round the roots can be removed when planting, or it can be left on, as it soon rots away without interfering with root growth. It is, however, advisable to cut the string and turn the top of the wrapping back.

If planting has not been done at once the balls should be plunged into a bucket of water for five or ten minutes, and then trench or planting holes should be filled with water, the planting being done as soon as it has drained off. Alternatively the plant can be put in, and the hole filled up with soil nearly to the top, and a good watering given. When this has drained into the soil the hole can be filled in. This is perhaps the better practice.

The above remarks apply to the planting of practically all young evergreen trees supplied with balled roots.

Privet (*Ligustrum ovalifolium*)

It has been said that privet hedges are the sign of an incompetent gardener, this being due, probably, to the ease with which privet is established. While the above statement is probably untrue, privet may certainly be described as the gardener's last resource, as there is probably no species which produces better results in difficult soils and situations. Privet grows almost anywhere. It is very hardy, grows quickly and stands smoke and fumes better than any other species. It will grow under light shade quite satisfactorily. As prices go today, it is perhaps the cheapest evergreen hedging plant on the market. It is a bad hedge as far as small gardens are concerned, as it produces masses of rootlets which spread rapidly and to a considerable distance.

Privet should be set in two rows, the plants being staggered 12 inches apart and 8 inches between the rows. Clipping should be done at least twice a year, preferably in May and September. If growth is good the number of clippings should be doubled, as very quick-growing privet is often difficult to get back into shape.

Privet is a much maligned plant, but a very useful one, since a good privet hedge will give more satisfaction than an inferior hedge of a more valuable species. There are two varieties, green and gold. The gold as a pure hedge is rather garish, but those who like a variegated hedge can mix it quite successfully with the more extensively used green variety.

Green privet today costs about 45s. per 100 for plants 1½ to 2 feet high. Golden privet is expensive, costing about six times as much as the green variety. If a good leafy base is to be obtained the plants must be cut well back for the first two years after planting out.

Lawson Cypress (*Cupressus Lawsoniana*)

This makes a useful hedge when conditions are good, and adapts itself to clays and chalky soils. It dislikes tree-root competition intensely, and, as a hedge, appears to suffer from 'drip', although this is not the case when it is used for underplanting as a single tree. It grows rapidly in good soil, stands clipping, and makes a hedge up to 15 feet in height, though tall hedges of this type are apt to become hollow near the ground in course of time. For this reason a sloping face should be aimed at, and hard cutting near the ground should be avoided. The bed should be deep and well dug. Plants 18 to 24 inches high set at intervals of 18 inches are best. Clip once a year in May or June, cutting back the tops lightly. Secateur pruning is better than with shears, as the cuts made by the latter show up very much on the flat sprays of foliage characteristic of this species. Plant in October or April.

Monterey Cypress (*C. macrocarpa*)

This gives a fast-growing, very green hedge, in fact the fastest growing of all. It requires warmth, and therefore does best in the south of England, especially in seaside districts. It is not particular as to soil, growing equally well on sand, chalk and clay. As a quick screen it is unequalled, but it is very liable to be killed by frost, especially if clipped late. It also has a way of suddenly dying off in large patches for some obscure reason, probably connected with root competition. It is liable at times to be badly damaged by insect attacks (generally an aphis).

Its extremely fast growth and its pleasant dark green appearance when clipped commend it to many people, but taken on the whole it is a bad hedge plant which, except for a quick temporary screen near the sea, should be avoided.

If this species is to be planted, pot-grown specimens should be used, set from 2 to 3 feet apart. Clipping is best done with secateurs. Hard clipping with shears eventually results in unsightly patches of dead brown foliage.

Mediterranean Cypress (*C. sempervirens*)

This cypress is said to make a good hedge, but in England at any rate such hedges are very rare if they exist at all, and specimen trees are far from numerous. This is all the more curious as 300 years ago it was what might be described as the standard, in fact the only, cypress found in the country. Evelyn, writing in 1664, says that 'we see it now in every garden rising to as goodly a bulk and stature as most which you shall find even in Italy itself'. It is probable that an alteration in climate rather than an alteration in taste is responsible for the marked decrease in general cultivation, as trees are still found growing satisfactorily, but only on warm, sheltered sites.

Sarawa Cypress (*C. pisifera*)

The Sarawa cypress (generally known as Retinospora) will make, and has made, quite a good evergreen hedge in this country, but it requires a certain amount of shelter. The leaf resembles that of Lawson cypress, but is rather more acutely pointed.

Two varieties also can be used. The first (var. *plumosa*) has a soft feathery appearance. The second (var. *squarrosa*) has pointed foliage which is silvery-green in colour, and makes the best-looking hedge of the three. *C. pisifera* is perhaps the hardiest, and stands clipping well. Var. *squarrosa* is really only suitable for sheltered aspects in the warmer parts of the country. It resents heavy clipping, and the light treatment necessary to keep it in good condition usually results in an unduly wide hedge. If treated in the same way as an ordinary evergreen hedge it is liable to die off in patches where cutting has got into old wood.

Giant Cedar (*Thuja plicata*)

This is one of the best of the evergreen hedges, and a comparatively rapid grower. It prefers a good clay loam, and will grow on thin soils over chalk or limestone rock, though on these it is not at its best. It is not really suitable for light soils.

It should be planted when 18 inches to 2 feet in height. Larger plants can be used, but little is gained by this, as the smaller specimens grow faster. As for all hedge plants a well-dug bed is required, and the trees should be put in 18 inches apart. Side pruning should begin early, but unless a very thick hedge is needed the leading shoots should be allowed to run up to the height required and not be cut back unless the growth is unusually rank. Clip in late summer.

Box (*Buxus sempervirens*)

This plant is more generally seen as a path-edging than as a hedge, but it is possible to raise box hedges to a height of 10 feet or so. Plants should be set 18 inches apart. They require plenty of manure, as they are hungry plants. Without this they are apt to go yellow and die off. Clipping should be done in summer. For hedges Common Box (*B. arborescens*) may be used, or better still *B. Handsworthii*, a wide-leaved variety with a strong erect growth, making an excellent hedge up to 5 feet in height. The variety used for edging purposes is almost invariably a dwarf type (*B. suffruticosa*), which can be brought up to a height of 3 feet if required.

Box has a tendency to go bare near the ground, especially on poor soils, and as has already been pointed out must be kept well manured.

Box is raised from cuttings of young wood with an inch or so of old wood attached. These may be transplanted as soon as rooted, and allowed to stand for two years before being moved again.

Euonymus (*Euonymus japonicus*)

Euonymus japonicus, with its glossy green leaves, is a common sight in the warmer seaside districts. It clips well, and is extremely hardy. It is indifferent to soil, and stands up to smoke and fumes. Like privet it is apt to be maligned by many good gardeners, but it is a really good utility hedge that can be successfully grown to a height of 6 feet or so. It is usually planted at 18-inch intervals. At the present time its high cost rules it out of most planting schemes. Euonymus is prone to damage by a type of mildew, but apart from this it has few troubles.

Yunnan Honeysuckle (*Lonicera nitida*)

This is a quick-growing hedge plant of dense habit, with small sparkling green leaves, which does best on medium soils. There is probably no hedge plant over which there is more difference of opinion than this Chinese honeysuckle. It has certain merits, being very quick growing and fairly hardy, and has the important advantage of being comparatively cheap. Its very much publicized demerits are, first, that it frequently becomes bare and weak at the bottom, and second, that the cut ends of the twigs die back after pruning, leaving small stubs. Lonicera frequently does get bare and weak at the bottom, so weak, in fact, that it is possible to shake 50 yards of hedge to and fro like a rope. In most of these cases it has been found that clipping has not been done regularly, and when done it has been too heavy. The same applies to the twig stubs. Lonicera hates heavy cutting, and this should be done lightly and often, especially when the hedge is young.

Damage by neglect is extremely difficult, in fact almost impossible, to repair. Once the bottom has died off there is little hope for the hedge, as cutting back hard will probably kill it completely.

Lonicera does not make a high hedge—about 4 feet 6 inches is the maximum—but old, carefully tended hedges are found in perfect condition and anything up to 5 feet in thickness. It is probably best to allow the hedge to grow to its maximum height without much top cutting, at the same time keeping the sides well trimmed in.

Established hedges occasionally need to be thickened or reduced in thickness. In the first case cutting back should be done on one side at a time only, the other being allowed to grow on. In the second case both sides should be cut, one more lightly than the other.

Lonicera is raised from cuttings quite easily. The plants should be set in single lines, and about 12 inches apart.

Clipping should start in late May, and finish in September. This operation should be carried out twice at least, and if growth is strong once a month will not be too often.

The Laurels

There are various types of so-called laurel that can be used for making semi-formal hedges. In practically all cases they require plenty of room, and being hungry plants are unsuitable for planting in small gardens or near flower beds.

Portugal laurel (*Prunus lusitanica*) is really a member of the plum family, despite its popular name. The leaves are large, and of a dark shining green colour. Leading authorities appear to differ about the value of this shrub for hedging. Coutts describes it as 'an attractive close-growing hedge'. Bean, on the other hand, calls it 'coarse and rough'.

Portugal laurel is fairly hardy, and on warm soils will stand up to many degrees of frost, but should be avoided in exposed situations or on chalky soils where there is much lime. It can be raised from cuttings of young wood with a heel of older wood attached. Small plants, not more than 2 feet high, should be used, set out 18 inches apart in May or September, as large plants move badly.

Pruning should be done in spring, and always with secateurs or a knife. Large-leaved shrubs clipped with shears invariably present an appearance more curious than beautiful.

Cherry laurel (*P. Laurocerasus*) is a quick-growing evergreen of which var. *caucasica* is perhaps the best for hedge making, being more erect in growth than the ordinary type. It is managed in the same way as Portugal laurel, but is not so hardy. It grows well on chalk soils, and must be kept well watered until established.

Laurustinus, really *Viburnum Tinus*, has been used for hedge making without much success, as it has a weak straggling form of growth that makes it very difficult to control.

Cotoneaster (*C. Simonsii*)

This is a hardy, semi-evergreen shrub with dark green, privet-like foliage, which makes a useful hedge up to 5 feet in height. It is a good type for small gardens, as it can be kept down to 12 or 15 inches in thickness. It stands clipping well, and if overgrown can be cut back hard without danger. Its hardiness is proved by the fact that it is used in forest-tree nurseries in the north of Scotland as a windbreak. Plants should be set in a single row,

18 inches apart, and when established clipped very early in spring or in late summer.

Rhododendron

The common rhododendron (*R. ponticum*) makes a useful hedge of semi-formal type on any soil that is free from lime. It is not a hedge for gardens, except very large ones, as it requires a good deal of room. It needs control, as it is apt to spread and become 'leggy' at the base, but careful pruning will keep the stems in check and prevent the base from becoming bare. Newly planted specimens must not be allowed to get dry, and an oak-leaf mould mulch is a great help. Rhododendron will stand shade and smoke. It is best planted as small specimens put in 2 feet apart. These plants should be compact, short-stemmed bushes, and not leggy specimens which will have to be cut back hard, if they are not to make things difficult later on. Specimen varieties can be used for hedge making, but their present-day cost is prohibitive except for those with a very deep purse.

Hemlock (*Tsuga*)

The Canadian hemlock (*T. canadensis*) is extensively used in the United States for making semi-formal hedges. At present its use in this country is rare, but there is an increasing number of hedges of Western hemlock (*T. heterophylla*) to be found. The species will grow satisfactorily on any fertile soil provided that it is well supplied with moisture. It will not grow on dry sandy soils. Transplants should be used, preferably 18 to 24 inches high, the trees being put in as a single row 18 inches apart. Little pruning should be done in the first two years, with the exception of the removal of straggling branches. Until the hedge is well established pruning should be done with secateurs or a knife, cutting back to a bud if possible, and never into old wood if this can be avoided. Prune once a year in early spring. This will allow the new shoots to grow through the summer, and preserve the graceful appearance characteristic of the species. If a formal shape is desired it may be necessary to prune three times a year instead of once. The last pruning should be carried out in late summer, so that the resulting growth may harden sufficiently to stand the winter.

The soil requires careful preparation before planting. Leaf mould or well-rotted manure should be worked into the soil in spring, after being allowed to lie on the top through the winter. Artificial manures are not desirable, but bone meal can be used at the rate of 2 ounces per yard of bed. In dry weather watering is very necessary with this species until it is well established.

Deodar (*Cedrus Deodara*)

The Indian cedar makes a most attractive hedge, which looks as if it were covered with blue-grey tassels. It can be managed as for hemlock. There is an excellent example of a deodar hedge on the Earl of Buckinghamshire's estate at Great Hampden. It was planted by the late A. G. Hobart Hampden, a one-time member of the Indian Forest Service.

The So-called Fir Hedges

The common spruce (*Picea excelsa*) can be made into a fairly satisfactory hedge. Strong transplants should be used, four to five years old, set if possible in a double line 12 inches apart, although a single line will do if space for the wider planting is not available. Pruning consists of removing over-long branches, and stopping back shoots (see SCOTS PINE, pages 62–3). Following the habit of its type spruce prefers moist heavy soils, and is not worth planting on dry, warm sites. Mulching and watering in dry weather are absolutely necessary for the first three or four years.

In the south and west of England, Monterey pine (*P. insignis*) can make an excellent hedge, rather rough but very pleasant to look at, and particularly well suited to a vegetable garden. It is treated like ordinary Scots pine (*q.v.*). Very good examples can be seen in the Forestry Commission's nurseries near Wareham in Dorset.

Evergreen Oak (*Quercus Ilex*)

This is a good hedge plant in the south and west of England on light, warm soil. It is a bad transplanter, which should be used ex-pots and planted in a single line 18 to 24 inches apart. It stands clipping well, and, carefully managed, makes a good thick, well-leafed hedge, which is particularly useful near the sea.

CHAPTER III

ORNAMENTAL HEDGES :
DECIDUOUS AND FLOWERING

DECIDUOUS HEDGES

Beech

Beech is the commonest and best of all deciduous garden hedges. It has many merits as a hedge maker. It grows on almost any soil, provided this is not too wet. It is easy to manage, and retains its leaves throughout the winter. It stands clipping well, and is comparatively cheap to buy. Beech can be grown to a height of 16 to 18 feet, and kept comparatively narrow at the base, so that ground is not wasted.

It is easily raised from seed, which should be gathered in November. Care should be taken to see that the seeds are well filled, as too often beech mast consists of light seeds with poor kernels which cannot produce satisfactory seedlings. They should be sown an inch apart, in drills, and covered to a depth of $\frac{1}{2}$ to $\frac{1}{4}$ of an inch. A pound of seed should not contain more than 2,000 seeds, and from this about 800 transplants ought to be raised. After two years in the seed-bed they should be transplanted and allowed to stand for another two years, the plants being set out 6 inches apart.

A beech hedge should be planted in two staggered rows 8 inches apart, the trees being about 15 inches apart. They must never be cut back hard, as is done with thorn. For the first two years after planting little attention is necessary, except weeding, and the cutting back of straggling side shoots. After that the hedge can be clipped in the ordinary way, preferably in July, as this encourages a second growth of shoots which makes the hedge thicker. If cut later there is a possibility of frost damage. As the hedge becomes established it is necessary to encourage height growth. This can be done by pruning back the longer growths, and tipping the shorter ones. For a really good dense hedge annual height growth should not be allowed to average more than 6 to 8 inches.

A characteristic of the beech is the way in which the dead leaves hang on the hedge during the winter.

Copper and Purple Beech

If variety is required the copper or purple beech can be scattered through the hedge. These varieties behave in exactly the same way as the common beech, and can be planted as a pure hedge if required. Such a hedge is extremely beautiful, as the contrasting shades of red, violet and purple do away with all monotony. There are very successful coloured beech hedges at Hidcote in Gloucestershire and Albury in Surrey.

Hornbeam

This was much used as a hedge in the past, but is now out of favour. Nevertheless it is a first-class hedge of its kind, especially on the heavier soils. It does not make as strong a hedge as beech, as the stems are not so stiff, but it stands clipping well, and presents a close, well-leafed appearance when properly looked after. The leaves hang on the hedge for the greater part of the winter.

Hornbeam grows well with thorn, and if planted at the rate of one to every six thorns helps to break the monotony of leafless twigs during the winter months. It can make a tall, thin hedge, and has been successfully used in industrial planting to conceal high, wired-in enclosures.

On the Continent it is frequently used as a hedge, and in Germany the plants are trained so as to cross one another at an angle of about sixty degrees. Where the stems touch, the bark is cut away and the stems bound together. The resultant grafting produces a hedge through which neither human being nor farm animal can pass.

At a distance it is difficult to distinguish between beech and hornbeam hedges. Close to they can be easily recognized by the leaf edge, which is smooth in beech and serrated in hornbeam.

For hedge making hornbeam is treated in exactly the same way as beech.

Myrobalan Plum (*Prunus cerasifera*)

This species was at one time considered to be likely to supplant the thorn as a farm hedge, as it was considered that it grew faster, was cheaper to raise, had spines and was rabbit proof. Time has shown that these ideas were not sound. It is certainly a fast grower and has spines, but it is not cheaper to raise than thorn, and it is certainly not rabbit proof, although given the choice a rabbit will attack the thorn first.

Myrobalan plum will grow on most soils, provided they are not too dry. There is a good fifteen-year-old hedge growing in a field belonging to Guinness's Brewery at Park Royal, near Acton.

Its cultivation is similar to that of thorn, and it is usually planted in two rows 9 inches apart with 12-inch intervals between the plants. Clipping should be done during the summer in late July or early August, and it is advisable to cut it back a little in December. It is said to do well on soils containing lime, and to be suitable for planting near the sea coast.

Where such a hedge has been neglected, and has become bare at the base, it can be cut back hard, the gaps being filled in with suitable stems laid down and fixed into the hedge.

The Thorn

The thorn makes a first-class garden hedge. It is hardy and stands clipping well, so that it need not take up much room. It stands smoke fairly well, and is thus well suited to planting in towns and suburban areas. The plant almost universally used for hedge making is *Crataegus monogyna*, the common thorn, and full details of its propagation and cultivation and management will be found in Chapter V.

Those who like thorn hedges, but want 'something different' could, when opportunity arises, try other thorns for hedge making. Beauty of flower cannot be taken into consideration, as so much flowering wood is taken off by the close clipping necessary for shape. Nevertheless there are always the leaves, and among the many varieties of thorn there are quite a number the foliage of which will produce a very pleasing summer or autumn effect. Few can be purchased today, but a certain number can be found as strong, healthy, berry-bearing trees. With a few handfuls of seed and a lot of patience results can be obtained which are well worth waiting for. The following should be worth trying:

C. Crus-galli. Cockspur thorn. Leaves change from dark green to scarlet in autumn.

C. prunifolia. Plum-leaved thorn. Leaves change to red and yellow in autumn.

C. orientalis. Leaves green above and sage grey below. This tree is quite common in the south of England.

C. tomentosa. Leaves orange-scarlet in autumn.

Finally, anyone wishing to raise a really terrifying hedge should try *C. macracantha.* A thorn 7 inches long was taken recently from a tree growing near London, and the average length of the thorns on most trees is about 4 inches.

FLOWERING HEDGES

These are hedges which, though pruned, are managed in such a way that the flowers form a decorative feature. With species used for this purpose shape must depend to some extent on the natural habit of the plant, as they cannot be cut back or clipped in the same way as beech or thorn. Moreover, the method of flowering plays an important part in cutting or trimming, as some species flower on the wood of the current year, and others on older wood.

Plants flowering on young wood can be cut back to two or three buds during the winter and up to March. The second group, blooming on old wood, must be treated differently. If they are cut back during the winter much of the flower is lost. In this case thinning out, and shortening back over-long stems is the practice usually followed, and this is done as soon as flowering is over. Syringa is a typical example of this class.

There are, however, certain plants which flower on old wood that come into bloom very early in the season; *B. stenophylla* is a good example. These produce their flowers before new wood is made, and if they are cut back when the flowers fade there is plenty of time for satisfactory new growth for the next year's flowering to be made.

A number of shrubs can be used for hedge work of this type, a few of the best being:

Berberis stenophylla

Perhaps the best of all rough flowering hedges. A very graceful grower, with long, slender arching stems covered with small, shining dark green foliage. The flowers are gold-yellow in colour, and very profuse. *B. stenophylla* does well on any fertile soil, and is suitable for town planting but it requires room, as it will grow up to 10 feet in height and 6 feet or so thick. One of the finest hedges of this species in the country can be seen in the grounds of the Park Royal Brewery near Acton, owned by Messrs. Arthur Guinness, Son & Co. This hedge is growing on sticky London clay. Planted fourteen years ago it is 1,000 feet long, and is kept down to about 7 feet in height. Over 600 plants were used for this hedge; the replacements were less than 5 per cent. in the first year, and there have been none since.

The best distance for setting plants is about 20 inches apart. 24 to 30 inches is not too far, but the hedge is naturally slower. This berberis flowers on the previous year's wood, and pruning, which must be done as soon as the flowers fade, consists in cutting back the longer growths, and taking out weak branches. Generally speaking the top of such a hedge can be easily managed, the chief care being for the bottom. Shears can be used, but with the greatest caution; individual pruning with secateurs is far safer and better. The bottom must have as much light as possible. The shortening of long sprays drooping from the top over the face of the lower part is therefore essential. If the bottom is allowed to become thin it is very ugly, and incidentally very difficult to improve.

Other berberis varieties that can be used are *B. Darwinii*, evergreen, with orange flowers and a foliage that resembles a miniature holly leaf. For deciduous berberis hedges there is the well-known *B. Thunbergii* that colours so well in autumn. This variety does not grow to any height, and is surpassed by var. *purpurea*, which is faster growing and better coloured, and can make a hedge of well over 4 feet if required. *B. Thunbergii* stands hard cutting back, and a bad hedge can be cut to the ground.

Sweetbrier (*Rosa rubiginosa*)

This rose has been in use as a hedge for over five hundred years, and as far as can be ascertained it was one of the first, if not the first, plants ever used to make a flowering hedge in English gardens. The flower is pink, and the stems tall and arching. The leaves have an attractive smell, especially after rain. Generally speaking sweetbrier, like most roses, requires post and wire support in the early stages, but if this is not considered desirable it can be kept pegged down in the line of the proposed hedge, which will help to form a strong bottom on which it can stand by itself. The 'Penzance hybrids' can also be used. They have a tall and bushy habit which lends itself to hedge making. The best varieties to use are probably Anne of Geierstein (dark crimson), Meg Merrilees (crimson and very free-flowering), and Lady Penzance (coppery-yellow). For a good thick hedge, which is necessary if the plants are to be shown to the best advantage, a double row should be planted, 30 inches apart. The soil must be well dug and well manured. Pruning is done in the spring, before growth starts, or may be confined to removing old wood and useless shoots, according to the class of hedge required.

Rosa rugosa

This is a strong-growing, erect rose with stout spiny stems. The flowers are single, and deep red in colour. It bears large red hips and will grow in any fertile soil, including thin clay over limestone. It stands clipping quite well, which, unlike most hedges, does not destroy its flowering value. It is at its best when lightly trimmed as a semi-formal hedge. The foliage turns an attractive yellow in the autumn. It should be planted in a single row 18 inches apart.

R. rugosa is also worth planting near the sea, but requires some shelter in order to do really well.

Quince (Chaenomeles lagenaria)

The so-called Japanese quince makes a good flowering hedge of the informal type, preferring a sunny, sheltered situation. The branches are dense and spiny, and make a formidable barrier. The foliage is a dark, glossy green.

The appearance of a quince hedge in flower can be much improved by mixing one or two varieties with the parent type, the flowers of which are red. Var. *alba semiplena* (double pink and white) and var. *nivalis* (pure white) are suggested for this purpose.

The planting interval is usually 18 to 24 inches apart, but a good hedge can be formed in time from plants 3 feet apart. Opinions vary as to the correct time for pruning, one school preferring to prune in May, another waiting till the end of July or early August. Quince hedges are not very common; the only one mentioned by Bean is in Ireland. There is one in the forecourt of Broadhurst Manor, Horsted Keynes, in Sussex.

Quince can be propagated from cuttings or layers, the latter being useful if the bottom has to be thickened.

MIXED HEDGES

Mixed hedges formed of different species can be very attractive, but they require considerable care in design, or rather, choice of species. Rate and type of growth must be reasonably similar, as must be the demands for light. To mix strong shade-bearers with light-demanding species will mean that in the long run the light-demanding species will probably be damaged, or even killed out. Evelyn's famous prescription for a holly hedge is a good example of this, the holly, a good shade-bearer, being mixed with thorn even at the low ratio of 1 to 6, eventually kills out the thorn, and a pure holly hedge results. Beech can be mixed with thorn, and helps with its dead leaves to create a greater impression of shelter during the winter. Although a shade-bearer, its growth is not so strong as that of holly, and it is nearer in habit to thorn. Privet can also be mixed with thorn if desired.

Mixed hardwood hedges can be made up of almost anything, and with careful attention to the foliage colours can be an ornament to any garden. A mixture of, say, thorn, beech, elm, oak and maple, an occasional copper or purple beech, planted together and kept clipped as a unit, can produce a bright colour scheme in the autumn of all shades of red, yellow and brown—a sort of horticultural tapestry.

Evergreens depend for their attraction on the colour and texture of their leaf. Yew and box is a good combination, but one that needs good management. Evergreen and deciduous mixtures are usually not very good, but at Hidcote Manor a mixture of holly, box, yew, beech and hornbeam has apparently

Lawson cypress as a boundary screen.

Cupressus macrocarpa as an orchard screen.

35

6. *A splendid example of box as a boundary hedge.*

7. *Holly makes a first-class garden hedge.*

36

8. *A semi-formal laurel hedge.*

9. *Clipped yew hedge at the back of a garden border.*

10. *Berberis stenophyl*
a 340-yard screen
Park Royal.

11. *Berberis stenoph*
as a dividing he
in the garden.

proved a great success, and is aptly described by Miss Sackville West [1] as 'being like a green and black tartan'. Generally speaking, however, the greater the number of species in a hedge the greater the number of problems there are to be solved, and unless the hedge builder is a very efficient horticulturist he will find it less troublesome, and will probably gain more than he loses, if he sticks to one species or variety of species.

Finally, to summarize:

Make certain that the species is suited to the soil. Do it well. Dig over to a depth of 18 inches at least, and break up the bottom if possible. On poor soils add leaf mould, or preferably farmyard manure, and get this below the level of the roots. Do not plant the trees in holes; dig the whole area, and so allow for root spread. Dig well in advance of the planting date to allow the soil to settle. Unless the plants are 'balled' spread the roots out as much as possible. Put fine soil over them, and work the plant up and down so as to get the soil settled close round the rootlets. Tread the trees in hard. More are lost by gentle treatment of this kind than by rough treatment.

When pruning flowering hedges remember the three classes and cut accordingly:

1. Flowers that bloom on new wood. Cut back in winter or early spring.

2. Flowers that bloom on old wood, at the same time as, or later than, the new growth is made. Thin back after flowering.

3. Flowers that bloom on old wood before new growth is made. Cut back after flowering.

TOOLS FOR ORNAMENTAL HEDGING

Tools for pruning hedges cannot be too good. Cheap tools of inferior steel waste time and often lead to crushed stems and mutilated leaves. Good quality tools are not cheap, but are well worth the extra money, as they give better service, and when properly cared for last much longer than less expensive ones. There are a number of good pruning tools on the market, and each person will have his own ideas on the subject, but the

[1] R.H.S. Journal, 74. 2.

c

following are recommended from experience gained in practical work.

Secateurs

Secateurs are a most important item in the hedge maker's collection. For ordinary garden work the 'Rolcut' has much to recommend it. For really hard wear where hedge work is concerned the Wilkinson Sword Company's 'Grower' pattern is ideal. Its cutting power is good, the cuts made are exceptionally clean, and it is comfortable to use.

Hedge Shears

The same company's W. 411 is good to own. The blades are heavy, the tool is well balanced and light in the hand, and cuts fast with a neat finish. The pruning notch at the base will cut through thick twigs with ease.

Light Saws

Saws are always useful for pruning the larger branches. There are various patterns, the commonest being the straight tapering type with teeth on both sides. This may save expense, but the side not in use is liable to damage other branches. Curved saws are easily obtained, and are to be preferred for pruning. Ordinary wood saws are slow in action, frequently 'bind', and should never be used on live wood.

Lopping Tools

If really efficient, lopping tools not only save time but are better for the hedge than a saw, as they leave a smoother surface. Probably the most powerful tool of this kind is the H. K. Porter 'Forester' No. 3, which will cut through a 2-inch green stem. The chief objection to it is, as might be expected, its weight. The H. K. P. 'Pointcut' Pruner has become very popular in this country, and is a comparatively light and efficient tool with a particularly clean cut up to $1\frac{1}{4}$ inches. Unfortunately these tools are made in the United States, and are at the present time very difficult to obtain.

Both these tools, in fact, while useful for hedge work are

really in the forest-work class. More easily obtainable is the Wilkinson 'Short-handled Lopper', a comparatively light tool with plenty of power. It is not only capable of cutting through ordinary branches of 1 to 1¼ inch diameter, but it can manage rhododendron branches an inch in diameter, than which there can be no better test for this type of tool.

In parks and gardens where considerable lengths of hedging have to be maintained, trimming by machine will prove far cheaper in the long run than manual work. For this purpose an electrically-driven machine called the 'Tarpentrimmer' is really good. It is very fast works seven or eight times as fast as hand-shears, and with a finish that is quite as good. It can be used quite successfully to trim hedges backed by mesh wire. Where electric mains are not available it can be worked from a portable generator, or if necessary a type can be obtained that will do a day's work from a fully charged 12-volt car battery. As its name implies this machine is a hedge trimmer rather than a cutter. The hedge by the roadside in Plate 1 is clipped with a 'Tarpentrimmer'. It is 450 yards in length, and two men get over it in a day and a half.

CHAPTER IV

TREE SCREENS

TREES can be usefully employed as screens. They can be used to hide houses, factories—in fact, anything objectionable to the eye of the beholder—provided that the beholder owns the land on which they are to be planted.

Tree screens may be anything from the magnificent one shown in Plate 14 to a row of a few fir trees at the end of the backyard. Not all trees are suitable for screen work. The ideal tree, of course, would be one that had no roots to interfere with the garden, and branches on two sides only and that grew about 40 feet high very quickly and then stopped growing altogether. As this tree cannot be obtained the only thing to do is to find the sort that has the best prospect of success.

Screens can be pure or mixed, that is to say of one species or of several. The latter may be more picturesque, but the former is generally much easier to manage, and unless the distance to be planted is very small those who want to plant screens would be well advised to use the same species throughout, especially if conifers are required.

Tree screens for urban use must as a rule be narrow, and if composed of trees that lose their leaves in winter the branching must be as dense as possible. They should be no higher than is absolutely necessary. For this reason normal height growth must be taken into consideration, and where small houses are to be screened trees of low-growing habit should be chosen. If this factor is neglected, 'topping', or cutting off the upper part of the crown, may eventually be necessary. Trees treated in this way lose their natural shape, and are apt to decay at the cut points, although if the cutting is carefully done topped screens can be effective and not unornamental for many years.

Screen trees are naturally required to be quick growing, but it must be remembered that quick-growing trees have the shortest lives and the shortest period of producing maximum screening effect. For quick effect poplars appear the obvious choice, but poplars have certain serious disadvantages, which are treated in detail later in this chapter.

In some cases, especially where boundaries are concerned, there may already be a boarded fence 5 to 6 feet in height. Where this exists the loss of lower branches characteristic of the pines is not important.

Screening with alternate slow- and quick-growing trees is sometimes practised, but it is not always successful. A common mixture is poplar and lime. The original idea is that the poplars will grow up quickly, and make a screen at once, and the limes will follow on. Eventually the poplars are taken out, and a lime screen is the result. This is sound in theory, but not so easy in practice. What generally happens is that the poplars, while growing in height, also spread out laterally. This means pruning practically every year. Young twigs are very sensitive, and unless the side cutting of the poplars is so heavy that it ruins their appearance the lime branches will become distorted and misshapen. Also, if the poplars are sufficiently close to make the early screen they get over the lime crowns and check height growth. Such a mixture can be managed, but the average householder whose wish is to make a screen that will produce the best effect with the least amount of trouble is advised to leave it alone. If, however, he is prepared to risk the wrath of his family by pruning or cutting out the poplars at a time when they appear to be doing the most good, then the mixture is worth planting.

Rooting habit also requires consideration, especially in small gardens. Most quick-growing trees, such as poplar, ash, elm, and, among the conifers, spruce, are surface rooting. These roots interfere with plant growth and take up moisture, and can be a great nuisance when digging a bed.

Complete screens are not always necessary, and a short row or narrow clump of trees which breaks up a building rather than hides it completely may be found perfectly satisfactory.

An alternative to a line of trees is the 'pruned screen'. This is a line of closely planted trees or shrubs allowed to grow in height, and kept in close check at the sides by early and frequent clipping. This is the type of screen so often used for hop gardens in the south-east of England. Such screens are very economical as regards space, as they need not be more than 18 inches in thickness, and for this reason they should commend themselves to the owners of small gardens. Lombardy poplar is the fastest of all, and has the quickest effect, as trees 6 feet high can be used, and topped when the required height is reached. The chief drawback to poplar for this purpose is the difficulty of keeping it dense at the bottom, as, being extremely light-demanding, it tends to shed its lower branches.

Beech and hornbeam make excellent screens of this type; in fact almost any broad-leaved tree can be used, although beech and hornbeam are the best for the purpose. The ordinary thorn will also make a first-class screen of this type up to about 12 feet in height, and can be kept to a thickness of about 24 inches. Thorn can be invaluable for the purpose in small gardens and among small houses.

Unless the garden is very sheltered 'pruned screen' heights should not exceed 15 feet, for as the young plants are closely planted, i.e. at 12- to 15-inch intervals, roothold is not too good, and wind pressure on the sides is considerable.

Where trees are to grow unchecked there are certain species that should be avoided wherever possible. One of these is ash. This tree grows very quickly, but has a sparse leaf system, and comparatively few branches. It is shallow-rooted, and will fill the ground around it with masses of fibre. Beech is naturally wide-spreading, casting a dense shadow under which few things will grow. Robinia is a graceful tree, but as it grows older it becomes gaunt and ugly. Most varieties of elm should be avoided, as their roots are hungry and grow to a very large size. They are liable to attack by elm disease which can kill, and has killed, quite young trees. Sycamore is another big, hungry tree with a fairly wide spread. It is, however, hardy, and easy to obtain. It should be mixed with other trees, as a single row of sycamore has no particular value, either as ornament or as a screen.

One of the best deciduous trees for screen planting is Norway maple (*A. platanoides*). It is very hardy, grows almost anywhere, and makes a good screen, particularly attractive in autumn when the leaves turn different shades of yellow and red-brown. Although the leaf is wide it is thinner and more attractive to look at than most wide-leaved trees. Another maple very well suited to this work is the field maple (*A. campestre*), a comparatively small tree with a compact head of small, heavily-lobed leaves.

The so-called box elder (*A. Negundo*) is a good tree for urban planting, usually not more than 30 feet high. The variegated variety has the same habit, but the leaves are a vivid green-white. A screen of this variety mixed with a few purple plum (*Prunus Pissardii*) makes a striking screen that would appeal to those who like bright colours. The combination, however, cannot be described as restful.

Mountain ash (*Sorbus Aucuparia*) is a suitable small tree with red berries, and rusty red foliage in the autumn. Another, much of the same type, is whitebeam (*S. Aria*), the leaves of which are green above and felted white below. Another most attractive tree of the same family is the wild service tree (*Pyrus torminalis*), which can be seen growing wild in the south-eastern counties. The leaves are large, the flowers are pleasant, and the colouring in autumn extremely good. All the above members of the pear family appear indifferent to soil, and stand town conditions well.

The thorns are generally put in the hedge class, but make excellent screens up to 20 feet or so. Normally crown spread is almost equal to the height, but they can be controlled by careful pruning. While the native thorn is rather dull there are several American varieties that combine beauty of flower and leaf. Of these the best, probably, is the plum-leaved thorn (*C. prunifolia*). The flowers are white and plentiful, and the autumn shades are rich reds and browns.

A comparatively new and attractive thorn which is on the market is *C. grignoniensis*. This is particularly useful as its spread is less and its normal height rather taller than most other thorns. It produces profuse quantities of scarlet berries, which remain on the tree right through the winter. For use as a screen these thorns should be planted from 8 to 10 feet apart. Pruning needs care, and should consist mainly in cutting out over-long branches and twigs. These should be cut right back to a main branch. If they are simply clipped or pruned back in the same way as a thorn hedge is cut they will throw out thick twig clusters from the ends of the cut branches which will give the trees an unnatural appearance when the leaf is off.

The birch can be used in screens if required. Its canopy is thin, but it is valuable for what might be described as lightening-up purposes.

The lime is one of the best screen trees, but unless it is to be pleached, or clipped, only the smaller varieties should be used. Of these *Tilia euchlora* is undoubtedly the best. Its height in this country seldom exceeds 30 feet, it grows reasonably fast and is seldom attacked by the aphides so frequently found on the common lime.

The round-headed trees, of which the above are perhaps the most suitable for screens, should be planted about 9 feet apart if early effect is desired. Normally they should be set about 16 to 20 feet apart, so that if closer planting is adopted every other tree must be taken out when the crowns approach each other too closely. If space allows for a double row the trees could be set 18 feet apart, in two staggered lines 8 feet apart, the bays in front being filled with shade-bearing shrubs such as laurustinus, rhododendron and the like.

Where space is limited, and single-line screens must be kept to a minimum width, fastigiate columnar trees must be used. Of these Lombardy poplar is by far the cheapest and fastest growing, and consequently the most frequently used. But of Lombardy poplar more will be said later.

While there are quite a number of fastigiate varieties of tree most of these are very rare, and apart from poplars there are only two or three obtainable, and not all of these in quantity at present. If the planter is prepared to risk the possibility of attack by Dutch elm disease (and provided that there is little or none in the district the gamble is a reasonable one) the Jersey elm (*Ulmus stricta Wheatleyi*) is probably the best choice. This tree has a narrow pyramidal habit, and can be planted as close as 10 feet apart. It is a tall-growing tree, but will stand 'topping' if necessary.

The two best types of fastigiate broad-leaved trees are the fastigiate beech (*Fagus sylvatica*, var. *Dawyckii*) and the fastigiate hornbeam (*Carpinus pyramidalis*), both admirable trees for narrow screens. Both are listed by nurserymen at reasonable prices, but to get sufficient for even a small screen would probably mean 'taking up a collection' all over the country.

Among evergreen trees it is not too difficult to find good types, the best being the Giant cedar (*Thuja plicata*) and Lawson cypress (*C. Lawsoniana*). Both of these make excellent screens, even as single lines. They can be planted at 5 feet apart, as trees 5 feet high, but just before the foliage of one tree touches the next every alternate tree should be removed. If by any chance this need for thinning has been overlooked and the trees have been allowed to grow into one another, it is probably best to leave them alone. Although they will not be as good as they might have been, cutting out alternate trees will spoil the screen as a whole, since there will be dead patches where the branches have grown into one another and death from over-shading has resulted.

The use of the biggest plants available will doubtless appeal to those who require immediate results. But the screen will probably be more successful if small trees of $1\frac{1}{2}$ to 2 feet are put in at 4 feet, and thinned when required. Moreover, it will often be found that in ten years' time the small tree is as big as, if not bigger than, the large one. The question of expense is also worth considering, the small trees costing exactly half the price of the larger ones. At the present time prices for Lawson cypress are more or less as follows per dozen:

> 18 to 24 inches, 20s.
> 30 to 36 inches, 40s.
> 54 to 60 inches, 120s.

These high prices are due to (1) increased wages, (2) scarcity of seed and (3) the fact that nurseries are only just getting back to the conditions that existed before 1939. Prices will probably come down to some extent, as is shown by the fact that Lawson cypress and thuja transplants, averaging 12 inches high, can be purchased for about 40s. per 100.

It may be taken as a maxim that the smaller the tree when it is finally planted the better it will do, and this refers to all conifers, and in fact to most trees.

Of other conifers for screens choice can be made between pines and spruces, the former being best for light soils and the latter for heavy ones. Among the pines the common, or Scots, pine is cheap to buy and a reasonably fast grower. It loses its lower branches easily, and after middle age much of its screening power is lost. The Austrian pine (*P. Laricio*, var. *nigricans*, a variety of the Corsican pine) is perhaps the best of all pines for this purpose. It is a rough-branching, irregularly shaped tree that holds its branches and dense foliage well down the stem. It makes quite a good one-line screen.

The Corsican pine also is a good screen tree, fast growing and with plenty of foliage. It will grow satisfactorily in smoky conditions, but is not so good as the Austrian variety, which is one of the best conifers for town planting. Both these trees can be planted on chalky soil, especially the Corsican pine.

The common spruce (*Picea Abies*, syn. *P. excelsa*) makes a good screen tree, as its shape is inclined to be pyramidal, its foliage is heavy, and it does not lose screening power as quickly as the pines. It is perhaps the best conifer to use on heavy loams and clays, but should be avoided in any situation where smoke and fumes prevail, as it resents these, and rapidly becomes ragged and unsightly.

The common larch (*Larix europaea*) loses its leaves in the winter. It is, therefore, not a good screen tree, except from the point of view of variety. It should be planted only on good soil, as otherwise it becomes stunted and unthrifty, and unpleasant to look at. A few specimens in a dark evergreen belt will help to lighten it up with delicate green foliage in the spring and yellow twigs in the winter. The Japanese larch (*L. Kaempferi*) is even more attractive, as its young twigs are light pink. It stands smoke much better than common larch, grows much faster, and is in every way a better tree to use.

POPLARS AND WILLOWS AS SCREENS

There are no species more popular for making screens than poplars and willows. The two outstanding advantages are, first, that the trees are comparatively cheap to buy, and secondly, that they are fast growing, in some cases so fast growing that a middle-aged man can plant them with every hope of seeing a tall screen before he reaches old age.

There are, however, certain drawbacks to the use of poplar as a really good screen. The poplar is a hungry and thirsty tree, especially a thirsty one. Its roots are long and straggling, with a great number of root fibres at the extremities. These fibres in their search for water invade drain pipes and inspection pits, sometimes filling them completely, and so interfering with drainage. What a man chooses to do about his own drain pipes is his own business, but poplar roots are no respecters of boundaries —a fact that must not be lost sight of. These matters, and others in connection with possible damage to property by roots are more fully dealt with in Chapter IX.

For these reasons poplars are not recommended for planting close to buildings, or anywhere close to house drainage systems. While it is impossible to lay down definite distances they certainly should not be planted within 20 to 30 yards of houses or drainage installations.

Another disadvantage of certain types of poplar, where urban screens are concerned, is the habit of throwing up suckers. These are young plants thrown up from points in the root system, and in some varieties form the only method of reproduction. Almost all poplars and willows are propagated from cuttings or suckers, as, in this country at any rate, fertile seed is seldom if ever found. These suckers can be a very great nuisance, as they may appear in considerable numbers close to the tree. They can also give trouble where trees are situated near lawns, as cutting over does not kill them, and they thicken up and interfere with mowing. Sometimes, especially where poplars have been planted on shallow clays over limestone, suckers may be seen growing in a straight line for distances up to 70 feet or more.

Another disadvantage of the poplars is the fact that they are so light-demanding that they shed twigs as well as leaves and flowers. One of the few varieties that do not give this trouble is the Lombardy poplar. Almost all the Lombardy poplars in this country are male specimens, so that under them the litter of fluff and coloured threads that forms part of the normal seeding is absent. (It should be mentioned that poplars and willows are dioecious, that is to say, having the sex organs on different trees. They are, in fact, the only two really well-known tree species in this country that have male and female flowers on separate trees. Other trees have hermaphrodite flowers, i.e. male and female organs in the same flower, or are monoecious, that is to say separate flowers of each sex are found on the same tree. Typical examples of this class are oak, beech and all conifers.)

Poplars and willows, especially the former, are insatiable in their demand for light. For this reason the lower branches get shaded out very quickly, with the result that these branches die and fall off. Much of the screening value of the tree is therefore lost, and it may be said of most poplars that their only use eventually is to screen the moon!

It must be admitted, however, that a row of black poplars in what might be termed late youth presents an attractive appearance, and makes an efficient screen not only in summer but in winter. After thirty years or so, and sometimes even earlier when growth has been unusually fast, the trunk starts to clean itself, and the crown develops into a collection of sparse branches, not particularly beautiful in summer and definitely ugly in winter. If, however, the short view is taken, and the trees are planted mainly for the benefit of the planter without regard to final development, poplars carefully chosen and sited make an efficient and cheap screen.

Poplars can, of course, be checked in growth by lopping and pruning, a method made easy by the fact that they stand up to it well, at any rate up to middle age, or, say, forty years. With old trees that have never been lopped or topped the cutting may be disastrous, at any rate on light, dry soils. To quote one case: a screen of trees about sixty years of age, growing on light soil, was lopped in late winter, and the spring was very dry. Out of fifty trees only two survived. The lack of water in this case was possibly due to the fact that the site was a churchyard in which there were many brick vaults. Nevertheless it presses home the point that soil conditions must be carefully studied before lopping old trees of this species.

Young trees will shoot extremely well and soon remake the screen. When this operation is carried out, side pruning should be done as well as topping, otherwise the branches tend to work into one another and die off.

Poplar timber is very soft. It decays very easily, and no really effective way of preventing cut tops from rotting back has yet been discovered. All that can be done is to take off the tops with a sloping cut, preferably towards the north-east. This stops rain from beating into the wood, and the slope helps it to run off. A dressing of thin tar and creosote mixed 50–50 can be applied, and then if possible a coat of some soft, knife-applied, thick bitumen. Even with this dressing decay eventually gets in, and the wood rots down towards the healthy shoots. The hold of these shoots on the trunk is thus weakened, and they break away. After summer gales a ring of broken shoots hanging down like a collar is quite a common sight in poplar screens. For the sake of safety, therefore, the shoots of poplars once topped should not be allowed to develop into branches of any weight.

Poplars kept as low screens and frequently cut back tend to develop unsightly swellings at the cutting points of branches. This is due to the practice of cutting back the shoots at the same place every time. Cutting should therefore be done in two ways. The first method is to take the shoots off several inches above the original pruning point. Several new shoots will develop on each old one, and these can be thinned out with a ladder and heavy pruners. Secondly, the branch can be cut below the original cut. Theoretically, this practice if carried out frequently would reduce the main branch to nothing, but five or six cuts in the life of the screen at this point are not going to reduce the length of the branch by more than 3 feet, and in any case some cuts should be made on the shoots themselves. This may mean more work, but it will certainly improve the look of the screen in winter, as old, neglected shoot-clusters are very prominent, very ugly and very unnatural.

Many of the objections to poplars do not extend to fastigiate varieties, especially the Lombardy poplar (*P. italica*, var. *pyramidalis*). This variety, the inverted-broom-like shape of which can be seen almost everywhere, possesses, above ground at any rate, most of the things that go to make a really useful screen. It is very cheap to buy, it is a very fast grower, its suckering powers are small and it is wind-firm and tidy. Apart from topping for height growth it needs no pruning, and it keeps its branches and leaves from ground-level up. On the other hand it is a hungry tree, with prodigious root spread, and, as is shown in Chapter IX, it is acquiring a bad reputation for damaging buildings on clay soils.

Poplars can be grown almost anywhere. They prefer a moist loam, but do well on heavy London clay, indeed on any clay. They will even grow on sands, provided they are not too dry. On sands the growth is slower than normal, and very great heights are not reached. This, incidentally, is an advantage, as a height of about 40 feet is quite enough to screen most houses.

The planting interval depends on the habit. Fastigiate, or upright growing trees, can be put in 6 to 8 feet apart in a single row, or in two staggered rows 5 or 6 feet apart, the trees being 10 feet apart in the lines. If a low screen is required up to 12 feet or so there is no reason why the trees should not be put in 5 feet apart, and kept topped and clipped to the height and width required. The wide-topped varieties need wider spacing, from 15 feet upwards. After planting the ground below should be kept well weeded, and growth is often improved by piling garden refuse or turf round the stem to a height of about 9 inches. This mulch should extend to a distance of at least 3 feet from the stem.

Poplars are usually hardy trees. Certain species are, however, liable to contract bacterial canker. This results in the formation of unsightly swellings on the branches. These do not kill the tree, but they are very unsightly, and may kill branches. The only other disease of any importance is the 'die back' disease, more or less confined to fastigiate types. This results in a gradual dying back of the crown, generally in patches, that spoils the appearance of the tree.

As regards insects, the Poplar Leaf Beetle and the caterpillar of the Puss Moth are occasionally found, the former being the more important. Both of them can be successfully dealt with by means of any reliable contact spray. Boring insects are usually confined to the larvae of the Goat and Leopard moths, the holes of which are easily seen. They can be dealt with by inserting a piece of cotton wool soaked in carbon disulphide, afterwards stopping up the entrance with clay. If the holes are not too deep a length of fairly stiff, well-pointed wire can be used to good effect.

Those who wish to raise their own trees (usually quite an easy matter) are referred to Leaflet No. 27, *Poplars*, issued by H.M. Forestry Commission.

The following is a list and brief description of the poplars most commonly found in cultivation.

Lombardy Poplar

A type eminently suited to screen work. Its merits and demerits have already been dealt with at length.

Berlin Poplar (*P. berolinensis*)

An attractive upright-growing tree with wide leaves. Not a suitable tree for planting in quantity, as individual growth varies very much. The tree is not really suited to this country, the climate of which is not usually warm enough during the growing season.

Canadian Poplar (*P. candicans*)

One of the 'balsam' poplars. Has frequently been planted in England. Dark green foliage with a whitish under surface. Particularly attractive after rain, because of its balsam-like fragrance. A fast-growing tree which is, however, not recommended for planting, as it throws up large numbers of suckers, and is often badly damaged by bacterial canker.

P. robusta

A very fast-growing hybrid poplar. In appearance a cross between the fastigiate and round-headed types, as its branches are ascending, although not to the degree of Lombardy poplar. It appears to be disease-resistant, and is well worth trying for screen work. As it is now being raised in large quantities for forestry purposes there should be no difficulty in obtaining it. *P. robusta* will grow in soils containing large quantities of lime. In very favourable circumstances it has been known to grow 50 feet in eight years. Such circumstances are not often to be found, however, and can never be expected in urban or suburban areas.

P. Bolleana (*pyramidalis*)

A variety of the White Poplar. This tree resembles the Lombardy poplar in appearance, but the general effect is that of a slighter, more elegant tree. The leaves are green above and white below. There is a fine specimen to be seen at Kew, but its history as regards growth in this country is not particularly good.

Black Italian Poplar (*P. serotina*)

The best-known and the safest type to use. A fast grower, very hardy, and indifferent to soil. Attractive as a screen when young, but gaunt and ugly in old age. Seldom if ever attacked by disease. Easily obtainable in quantity.

White Poplar (*P. alba*)

A beautiful tree, with dark green leaves covered with white felt on the underside. Unfortunately not a good tree for tall screens, as the branches are brittle, the trunk cleans itself early, and the tree is one of the greatest offenders in throwing up suckers. It makes a very good boundary tree mixed with other species, as the contrast is very striking. The grey poplar (*P. canescens*) is often mistaken for *P. alba*, but can be distinguished by the grey surface of the underleaf and the diamond-shaped markings on the trunk. Otherwise it resembles the white poplar very closely. Where space is available these two poplars can be used to make quick, rough, low screens, and will stand hard lopping.

Black Cottonwood (*P. trichocarpa*)

A very fast-growing tree with attractive foliage, green above and white on the underside. In spring, and especially after rain, the leaves have a pleasant balsamic smell that extends for a considerable distance. Young trees are pyramidal in shape, and well covered with branches and leaves. As the tree gets older the crown becomes angular and sparse, with large branches that are easily broken by the wind. As it grows older the tendency to throw up strong suckers is very marked. As a *temporary* screen to last for from fifteen to twenty-five years this tree can be quite useful, and if required the screen life can be prolonged by topping.

2. *A well-kept hedge of privet, one of the most useful and easily established of hedging plants.*

3. *A young hedge of purple beech.*

14. *A screen of limes in Copenhagen.*

15. *Temporary wind-screening for newly planted evergreens.*

16. *A pleached lime-screen in summer.*

. The same screen in winter, showing how such screens should be trained.

57

18. *Windbreaks from the air.*

This has to be done fairly frequently, as the wood rots quickly at the 'topping point', and once branches close to this point exceed a diameter of about 4 inches they seem to break away very easily. Left to itself the tree grows to 100 feet and over in favourable situations.

The Willow as a Screen

The common white willow can be used as a screen tree, but is not very suitable for houses, as its natural habit is very spreading. It is very useful as a quick screen for industrial buildings of considerable length, when pollarded or topped at an early age. It then puts out a mass of semi-vertical shoots which grow to a considerable height, and throw out leaf all along the stems. Eventually the spreading habit asserts itself, and unless set off by large blocks of building it looks top-heavy. Plate 2 shows a hedge of this kind screening a factory. Rooted sets were planted 12 feet apart about sixteen years ago, and topped at 7 feet as soon as planted. This screen is now over 40 feet high, and apart from the pruning out of broken or straggling branches has had no attention at all.

If a very thick screen is not required on a site where there is plenty of moisture the cricket bat willow (*Salix alba* var. *caerulea*) can be used. Rooted sets or cuttings are put in at 15-foot intervals, and there are few trees that need less after-care where screens are in question. The habit of the tree is ascending, the leaves are bluish-green. If a quick-growing screen is required at a moderate cost this variety of willow is worth considering.

On flat land where space is available the weeping willow (*Salix babylonica*) makes a most effective round-headed screen. It takes up a good deal of room as it must not be cut back in any way. Trees should be planted about 18 feet apart.

PLEACHED SCREENS

The 'pleached screen' is derived from the 'pleached alleys' which were a common feature in the gardens of three hundred years ago. These consisted of trees trained over arches in such a way as to make a shady walk during the heat of the summer.

D

The trees most generally used for this purpose were lime, wych-elm, ash, hornbeam and in later years, plane.

Pleached screens may be described as aerial hedges supported on tree stems. They consist of trees planted closely together, the branches of which are trained and clipped in exactly the same way as an ordinary hedge. While now comparatively rare in this country they are still much in use on the Continent.

Pleached screens should be used much more in small gardens, where space is important. They form a compact barrier more efficient than any narrow planting of trees, they can be run up to almost any height, and take up little lateral space. With very tall screens clipping is, of course, expensive, but the cost of clipping a screen about 15 feet high is comparatively moderate.

While various trees can be used, the best and easiest is undoubtedly the lime. This species stands cutting well, and the new shoots grow quickly and straight, making training very easy. Trees with very straight stems 5 to 6 feet long and good heads should be planted at a distance of 8 to 10 feet apart, and allowed to grow untouched for two or three years in order to become well established. When they are 10 to 12 feet high they can be topped back, and the side branches slightly shortened to encourage branching. New shoots can be trained along thick wire, or better still along bamboos, being loosely tied in with tarred cord. Front and back branches which are not suitable for bending into the screen must be cut very well back. They should be cut closer to the trunk than the final edge of the screen will be, to allow for clipping or pruning that will encourage small shoots to make the face thick.

It will be found that the tendency of the shoots is to grow upwards, so that if additional height is required all that is necessary is to tip back the top shoots when pruning the hedge in order to get thick twiggy growth, and consequently plenty of leaf; in fact the hedge should be treated in the same way as any hedge of tree species established in the ordinary way from the ground.

CHAPTER V

AGRICULTURAL HEDGES

THE traditional plant for agricultural hedges is the white-thorn, which over many generations has proved that in most situations it possesses all factors necessary for a satisfactory farm hedge. The main essentials may be summarized as follows:

1. *The hedge must be quick growing.*
Thorn hedges can be produced in five or six years.

2. *It must have a long life.*
Thorn hedges properly looked after and trimmed will exist for well over fifty years, and if plashed may last for a century or more.

3. *It must be stock proof.*
Thorn hedges with their short, stiff growth and thorny branches make the best live hedge with this quality.

4. *It must be hardy.*
Experience shows that no hedge plant can withstand frost or wind more efficiently than thorn.

5. *It must be cheap.*
Nothing is cheap today, but no reliable hedge-making species costs less than thorn.

6. *It must stand cutting.*
No species will stand the cutting, twisting and general distortion of stem necessary in hedge laying as well as thorn.

7. *It must be adaptable to the soil.*
There are few soils to which the thorn is not adaptable, at any rate in England.

8. *It must be of a strong healthy type, not liable to attack by insects or disease.*
Apart from occasional attacks by leaf eaters thorn seldom suffers.

9. *It must respond well to repeated pruning.*

No hedge plant stands up to pruning better than thorn.

10. *It must be thick enough to keep out wind, and compact enough at the bottom to stop ground draught.*

Properly kept thorn hedges are heavily leafed from top to bottom, and afford excellent shelter.

11. *It must be a species not usually eaten by animals.*

Apart from young shoots, which may need fencing off, thorn hedges are seldom damaged in this way.

Blackthorn is sometimes planted as a farm hedge. It stands cutting, can be plashed easily, and is better for gapping. The chief objection to the use of this species is its tendency to throw out suckers rather than shoots when cut, with the result that, if neglected, patches will be found growing out into the field.

Other species that have been used for rural hedges are beech, holly, hornbeam and myrobalan plum. The planting and treatment of these have been dealt with in a previous chapter under garden hedges.

Of all these holly is probably the best, doing well in practically any soil except wet, heavy clay. It has, however, few properties that the thorn does not possess, and is best used for patching gaps under trees, as it stands shade very well.

Beech makes an excellent hedge, and although it has no thorns a strong, well-trimmed beech hedge will make quite a good barrier. It is probably the cheapest hedge today, as although so-called 'hedging beech' is expensive, ordinary forest transplants can be used with success. But again, unless there is some excellent objection to the use of thorn, beech should not be used where cattle are likely to be found as the shoots are very liable to be eaten off.

Hornbeam is similar to beech, but is better on the heavier types of soil. It stands frost and exposure better than beech.

In the drier parts of England, Scots pine is occasionally used as a farm hedge. It will grow rapidly, and makes quite a useful rough hedge. The best plants to use are two-year–two-year trees (i.e. those which have stood for two years in the seed beds and the same time in nursery lines) planted about 2 feet apart. Pruning is done by cutting back the annual shoots to one-third of the full length. This encourages side branching, and keeps the trees compact. If a branch must be shortened it should be cut back to a bud in the centre of a branch whorl.

The Propagation of Thorn

Thorn quicks are raised from seed. The 'haws' should be collected in autumn, mixed with sand and allowed to remain for a year, by which time the flesh should have rotted away. The seed is then sown in a well-dug bed and in shallow drills about 1 inch deep and 9 inches apart. During the next two years the young plants should be carefully weeded. No protection from sun or frost should be necessary.

The two-year trees are then transplanted to another bed and set 4 inches apart, the lines being at 8- to 10-inch intervals. They stand for two years, the only cultivation needed being careful weeding. In some cases the plants are cut down close to the ground after one year in the transplant lines in order to make them more bushy.

Young thorn quicks are obtainable from most nurseries, and it may be considered preferable to save three or four years by purchasing them as plants ready to go out.

Making the Hedge

Practically all new hedges nowadays are planted on the flat. The bed in such cases should be 3 feet wide, the central foot being 18 inches deep and the remainder 1 foot deep. Trenching today is expensive. Forty years ago, when wages were 14s. 6d. per week, it cost 12s. 6d. per 100 yards. With today's wages and type of labour it will probably cost nearer 90s. Planting at six plants to the yard[1] will now cost 25s. per 100 yards, or say 1s. 3d. per yard in all. An average price would, however, be nearer 1s. 6d. per yard if carting, lost time, etc. are included. The price for planting is about 3d. per yard (an actual price paid in 1949). It is interesting to note that this price follows the sixfold rise in wages since 1905, the price for planting at that time being one halfpenny per yard.

---

[1] Pre-war practice was nine plants per yard, and this is preferable if expense is no object.

At present prices the planted hedge would, therefore, cost much as follows per 100 yards:

	£	s.	d.
Preparation and planting at 1s. 6d. per yard . .	7	10	0
Quicks 600 at 30s. per 100 (commercial nursery price)	9	0	0
	£16	10	0

or, say, 2s. 6d. per yard.

Here again the effect of the rise in labour over forty years is shown, the cost per yard in 1905 being 5d., or one-sixth of the present-day price.

If, on the other hand, plants are raised at home and the bed is got out largely by mechanical means there is no doubt that the saving, apart from four years' delay, will be very considerable indeed. Expense can also be cut to some extent by buying two-year seedling thorn and growing them on. Such plants will probably do far better than older ones planted straight from the commercial nursery.

If young thorns are to be used to replant or fill up an old hedgerow where the soil is really poor, as much old soil as possible should be removed and new soil added, preferably as a compost with leaf mould. A dressing of short farmyard manure will also be useful.

Early Treatment

Treatment after planting varies, and there seems little to choose between methods. Some people grow the hedge on for four or five years, and then cut it back to shape. Some cut the young plants back to within 2 or 3 inches of the ground as soon as planted. Others again cut them back after one year's growth, to a height of 2 to 3 inches from the ground, and this is probably the best method to adopt.

After that, treatment depends on whether the hedge is to be kept as a trimmed hedge as long as possible, or whether it is to be 'laid' at the earliest possible opportunity.

In the first case the hedge is gradually trimmed into shape by annual cuttings, generally done with a 'switch bill'. In the second, the plants are allowed to grow more or less unchecked until they reach the height which will allow of efficient 'laying' or 'plashing'.

Management

If a row of thorns is allowed to grow unchecked it will grow upwards and remain fairly thick for a number of years. After it reaches a height of about 10 to 12 feet it will start to 'bush out' at the top, the stems will gradually thicken, and it will finally revert to its normal tree form. In such cases it will usually be found that various stems have been smothered out in the course of time, and that lower branches tend to die off, leaving the bottom rather open. If left to itself the planting will usually finish up as a row of trees in which all the foliage is at the top. Such a planting may produce a little shade, but very little shelter.

To obtain a hedge thick from top to bottom it is therefore necessary to control it by pruning, which encourages new growth, keeps the hedge thick, and prevents the branches near the ground from being 'shaded out'.

The two most usual ways of obtaining a satisfactory hedge are by (a) simple pruning or trimming, and (b) cutting and laying. The second method can be used to produce a good hedge in cases where a trimmed hedge has through neglect or other cause become thin and open near the ground.

A 'trimmed' hedge is natural in appearance, being a barrier of twigs and leaves growing in the ordinary way, and kept in shape by cutting at frequent intervals. A plashed or cut-and-laid hedge is one in which the branches are kept long, so that they can be either bent over and wound in and out between stakes, or, as in the Midlands, laid out at an angle to the fence and then staked and bound at the top. Such hedges are seldom more than 3 feet 6 inches in height, whereas a trimmed hedge may be 6 to 7 feet high, but more usually, as far as agriculture is concerned, about 4 feet or so.

Shape

There are at least a dozen shapes to which a hedge can be cut, but for agricultural purposes these can be reduced to one. The triangular or 'hogged mane' shape is undoubtedly the best. It is easy to cut, and as the lower branches get plenty of light, growth is good and density at the bottom is preserved. Square-sided and square-topped hedges, which are too often seen, are bad hedges. Snow collects on the top and breaks the twigs, and they get thin at the bottom very easily unless given an amount of care which is not warranted on the farm.

With a well-planted hedge on good soil a height of 3 feet 6 inches to 4 feet should be aimed at by the sixth or seventh year. A three-year hedge should be cut back to about 18 inches high and 12 inches thick. After that the new growth should be shortened to 6 inches or so each year. Rapid increase in height is undesirable, as this tends to produce long, thin and comparatively weak stems.

During this period the branches are cut or switched in each year with a sharp hook or bill. The usual type of switching bill is very light, weighing about 2 pounds, with a blade 7 to 8 inches long and $2\frac{1}{2}$ inches wide. With a single-bladed tool such as this cuts are always made where possible in an upward direction. Switching is usually done twice per year, and preferably in the summer, as it is more expensive when done in the winter.

Trimmed hedges properly looked after may last for many years. Eventually, however, the bottom starts to open, and growth slows down. The time when this happens is dependent on such factors as past management, type of soil and exposure. The time has then arrived when cutting and laying is necessary if a satisfactory hedge is to be kept.

If a hedge has been planted with the idea of cutting and laying as soon as possible, this can generally be done when the hedge is 6 to 8 feet high. If a comparatively young and properly kept 'trimmed' hedge is to be dealt with, it must be left uncut for three or four years in order to get sufficient length on the stems.

Cutting and laying is a highly skilled operation, which to the beginner abounds in difficulties and problems that cannot be learnt from books. It will be found, moreover, that while the general principles are the same everywhere, hedgers in different districts have different ways of obtaining more or less the same result.

Generally speaking, cutting and laying, or plashing, is carried out much as follows. Weeds having been cleared away from the base of the hedge, the hedge stakes are selected. These may be straight, vertically growing stems, spaced from 2 to 3 feet apart and topped at hedge height. If sufficient live material cannot be found, dead stakes must be used, and in Leicestershire and the surrounding counties this is considered to be the best practice. Any species is suitable for this, but if willow is used it must be peeled at the base, otherwise it will shoot and damage the thorns.

The plashers, or stems which will make the actual fence, are then selected, and those not required for this purpose are cut away, preferably with an upward cut, at a few inches above ground. These stumps have their uses, as they will eventually shoot and help to make a good bottom. The selected plashers are then cut into, a few inches from the ground. Where possible this cut should be made upwards, and only sufficiently deep to allow the stem to bend to the angle required without splitting. For thin stems a single cut is usually sufficient. Heavier stems will generally require a notch cut out. Cuts are sometimes made downwards, so that the stem is almost split to the ground. The pointed piece on the vertical section of the stump is then taken off with an upward cut. This method is easier, but is not the best, as moisture trickles into the crack, and the plasher rots away at the base. With the upward cut, moisture runs off without lodging and the plasher lasts much longer.

After the cut is made the plasher is either wattled in and out of the stakes at an angle of about forty-five degrees, being topped if hedge height is reached, or laid outwards at an angle from the roots (see Plate 21). In this case it will be seen that the stakes are set about 2 feet apart and well back, the plashers being laid in front; the ends only are packed through the stakes.

Brush and twigs are usually cut off the stems on the side where the hedger is working, the remainder being packed in as far as possible on the side from which most damage is to be expected from stock. For this reason the work is invariably done on the side which requires least protection and so usually away from the ditch.

Branches should be packed so as to keep the hedge thick, but sufficient room should be left to admit light and air, otherwise growth will suffer.

The hedge top is kept down by 'heathering' or 'binders'. These generally consist of thin hazel or willow rods about 8 feet in length, which are laced round the stake tops in pairs. This is done by laying the first rod behind the first stake, and then round the front of the second stake, and so on. The second rod is placed behind the second stake, twisted round the first rod, and then placed in front of the third stake, and so on. The ends of the rods are also twisted together. The binding is then forced down to the correct height, and the projecting end of the stake cut off.

As a general rule replashing should be done at intervals of from eight to ten years. Hedges are trimmed back every year for five or six years, and then allowed to grow unchecked for three or four years so that the shoots will be more suitable for laying. In the Midlands trimming is frequently dispensed with.

No treatise on agricultural fences could be considered complete without a reference to the famous Leicestershire 'bullfinches', for many years used for keeping in the heavy bullocks of the Midland grazing areas. Although the use of them is declining, their position in the annals of British agricultural fencing is so prominent that they should not be allowed to sink into oblivion. Possibly, too, somebody with plenty of money behind him might wish to construct one! One of the best descriptions of the construction and management of the bullfinch is to be found in a paper on the subject written by W. J. Malden some fifty years ago. The methods laid down are as sound today as they were then, and no apology is made for quoting them *in extenso*.

The ditch is cut about three feet wide and two feet deep, raising a bank about a foot high. It is composed of the turf turned in green part downwards, covered with several inches of fine soil, obtained from the bottom of the newly formed ditch. In this bank the quick or whitethorn is planted by cutting out the lines and placing each set about nine inches apart in two parallel rows, the same distance apart. The age of quick is generally two-year seedlings which have been transplanted in nursery rows and grown on there two years longer; this process ensures plenty of short fibrous roots near the surface, and stiffens the stems, from which the young growth is made when cut down to about three inches from the surface of the soil. They are then allowed to grow up six to eight feet high, which takes, in most cases, about five years to accomplish—ready for cutting and layering, commonly called laying. During the whole of this time the new fence is protected by a 'post and rail' fence on one or both sides, according as the land adjoining is arable or not, as the young hedge must be protected from the cattle, and be allowed free and undisturbed growth.

The process of laying is done at any time during the winter by cutting off the back row, or that on the land side, about three feet from the ground, selecting the strongest rods, trimming them and leaving them about two feet apart to act as stays, through which the whole length of the front row is drawn down and interlaced to secure them from springing upwards, and causing them to remain in the position in which they are placed. The layers must be split a little more than half through, about nine inches from the ground, on the side opposite to the direction of laying, and be wattled in at an angle of about thirty degrees from the ground. By selecting the best of these and turning the brush or thorny parts towards the land and away from the ditch, a very strong and well-bound fence can be secured, all superfluous thorn parts being cut away, to leave the whole mass even and regular. These will produce fresh growth in both rows, and grow up between the layers and further strengthen the whole living mass. In the old fences when plants have died through old age or other cause, stakes of ash, thorn, elm and any other available kind of timber (except willow or elder) may be used as stays, and in such cases the layers of old hedges sometimes being few in number, it is necessary to take great care not to cut away any that might be required, and to make up for such deficiency as occurs by inserting dead wattles. The ditches are then filled with the surplus cutting of thorn, which keeps the cattle out and helps to protect the young growth of the fence. The object of placing the brush or thorny extremities of the layers on the land side is to form a wall against the stock. The brush and wattle are bound carefully along the top, with a binder made by interlacing long strips of young hazelwood or brambles, from stake to stake.[1]

[1] *Journal of the Royal Agricultural Society of England*, pp. 92–3. 1899.

Treatment of Old, Neglected Hedges

The method adopted for improving old, neglected hedges must vary according to the condition of the hedge. Too often a hedge consists of rough, big, overgrown stems, bushy at the top and with few live branches at the bottom. Such fences are often full of gaps as well, and it is generally the number and extent of the gaps that determine the course of action to be taken. If the gaps are wide and numerous it will probably be wisest to grub the hedge out altogether, and if a new fence is to be made, to site it, if possible, backward or forward of the old line, as the soil of the hedge is bound to be worn out. Grubbing out in such cases may be economic, as by throwing two fields together, it may make field-working easier and cheaper.

If it is decided to retain the hedge, which although thin at the bottom and inclined to be gappy has a satisfactory amount of fairly straight growth, especially near the gaps, plashing will probably produce a good result. But to get a good result means skill, patience and ingenuity. Before starting it will be necessary to clear away all weeds and dead wood, especially elder, ivy and bramble. Gaps too wide to layer must be filled, either by strong live plants or by post and rails, which should be placed on the hedge line. Larch 'half rounds' are good, but where obtainable, split chestnut is better as it lasts so much longer. Narrow gaps should be fenced, if actual layering is not possible, because if plants are put in they get overgrown and crushed out very quickly. If they must be put in, holly will probably be more successful in the long run than thorn, as it stands shade far better.

When laying any type of hedge it should be remembered that the real hedge is the young growth, and not the stem or stake. Quite often far too much wood is worked into the hedge with the result that growth inside is prevented or even killed, and the hedge as a whole is weakened.

An overgrown hedge is sometimes cut to the ground. This can be done if the stubs are not too old, and are likely to re-shoot satisfactorily. In such cases the bed should be well cleaned, and the stubs earthed up. The gaps must be dug up, fresh soil added, and strong young transplants put in. This method is easy, but it is some years before the hedge becomes stockproof.

If the hedge is wide and spreading with few gaps the simplest solution is 'ribbing' or 'siding back'. This is usually done with a 'ribbing bill'. In this operation the hedge is topped, and then cut to within about 6 inches of the main stems on each side. It is a strain on the stems, and one side only should be done at one time, and preferably in March or April if the situation is exposed. In other situations any time during the winter will do, except in frosty weather. The remaining side can be done the following year, or better still the year after that.

Where the hedge has been planted in two lines, and the stems are healthy and not too large, one side can be cut to the stump, the other being only slightly trimmed of straggling growth or not touched at all until the cut side has grown up. This method produces a thick bottom, but there are obvious risks such as weak growth caused by shading from the uncut side. The method of ribbing up the sides without cutting down is therefore safer, unless thick bottom growth must be made. In either case a definite slope from the top should be aimed at.

When making up gappy hedges on farmland, advantage should be taken of the occasional species that may have crept in. Such are English maple, beech and even elm, all of which will, if taken early enough, trim very satisfactorily into bush form. Elm suckers are often found in quantity where old hedgerow elms have been felled, and on old banks can be trimmed in such a way as to fill up comparatively long lengths of fence.

In the south-east of England coppice growth is occasionally used for fencing purposes around woodland, hornbeam being a common species for this type of semi-live hedge. The poles are allowed to grow up to about 12 feet, and are then slashed and laid towards the next stool. If this is carefully done a fairly serviceable live side on the field edge can be maintained for some years, but growth is almost entirely confined to the outside. As the layers all come from stools set at wide intervals there is usually too much wood and too little twig growth in the fence.

Repairing Banks

Attempts to improve hedges set on banks will often be wasted labour unless attention to the bank is given as well. There is a tendency for the soil to wash downward, and a ditch can be almost completely filled up in bad cases. This 'washing down' exposes the root tips, which die away, and this weakens the vitality of the plants and allows strong winds to rock the hedge. Such hedge banks may be sodded, as follows:

Cut the bank away from just below root-level to a depth of 3 to 4 inches, the cut extending down the bank for 12 to 15 inches. This makes a key for the new turf. Sods are then cut from the ditch, about 12 inches long, 8 inches wide and 4 inches deep. These are laid grass side uppermost along the lower edge of the cut and well beaten down, with the top edge bevelled off. This will leave the upper portion of the cut still exposed. Sods similar to the first but an inch or two narrower are then cut and beaten into place on the upper portion near the roots. The bottom edge of these should overlap the upper edge of those first set in position, and the sod in this case should be placed grass downwards. Soil from the ditch should then be placed on the bank and among the tree roots. In the Midlands, where ditches are almost invariably found, the usual practice is to repair the bank by throwing the soil back from the ditch when it is cleaned out, usually at the time when laying is being done.

Burnt Hedges

In dry weather hedges may be damaged by fire. Properly kept hedges with a clean soil below are generally less damaged than rough or neglected hedges with a thick layer of old leaves and rubbish round the roots. With a clean base to the hedge fire may pass quickly without producing more damage than external scorching, but with dirty hedges slow burning sets up enough heat to kill the trees at the base. In recent years there has been an alarming increase in damage of this kind, due to straw-burning after cutting with a combine.

In such cases the only thing to be done is to leave the hedge until the end of the next growing season so that the actual areas of damage can be discovered, and then cut hard back.

Thorn stems blackened at ground level may be only scorched, but if the heat has been sufficient to kill the cambium, or growing layer below the bark, there is nothing to do but to cut right back to the ground.

THE COST AND MAINTENANCE
OF THORN HEDGES

Cost

The cost of planting thorn hedges has already been given as approximately 2s. 6d. per yard. In this case purchased plants were used. If plants are raised from seed on the farm or estate there seems no reason why the actual cost of plants should exceed £4 0s. 0d. per 1,000 against the £14 0s. 0d. charged today by commercial nurseries. In time this somewhat fantastic price will probably come down, but even so it will never closely approach the cost incurred by raising plants at home.

If the ground is first broken up by mechanical means the cost of spade work will be made lighter, and the cost of preparation reduced by at least 25 per cent. In such circumstances the cost of preparation and planting should not exceed 1s. 2d. per yard. The total cost of the hedge would then amount to approximately 1s. 9d. per yard.

Maintenance

Weeding and trimming costs today anything from 2s. to 6s. per chain, and 3s. 6d. may be taken as an average, although in some districts the price can be as low as 2s. For cutting and laying the cost is difficult to lay down, as it depends on the period that has elapsed since the hedge was last laid, the way in which the work was done, and last but not least the treatment it has received since the last time the work was done.

Costs vary from 15s. to 50s. per chain, the lowest price being paid for young hedges, and the highest for big overgrown ones. A fair average for the country as a whole would be about 30s. per chain, equivalent to 1s. 4d. per yard. It is generally considered that a chain and a quarter is a good day's work, and if a man does much more than that he is either doing bad work or has an unusually easy hedge to deal with. The question of lost time owing to wet days must not be overlooked when cutting and laying is concerned. Work is difficult and undesirable in wet weather, or when the hedge is wet. In such circumstances gloves are soon ruined, and good hedging gloves are expensive.

Fencing against stock may be necessary, and it may also be necessary to guard against rabbits. In the latter case a rabbit-proof fence on both sides is required. For stock alone, if the hedge is between arable and pasture, a single fence only will be needed.

When erecting fences much expense can be saved if a 'Driveall' is used. With this tool a post with a top diameter of 5 by 6 inches can be driven 3 feet 6 inches deep in less than four minutes in deep soil. In such soil three men have been known to drive one hundred posts (4½ by 4½) and put up four strands of wire as well in one day. In this case the posts were 6 feet apart, so the cost for labour per 100 yards of completed fence was only 30s., and for the fence erected about 1s. 6d. per yard.

The specification and cost of a cattle- and sheep-proof seven-wire fence recently erected on good driving ground with the help of a 'Driveall' is as follows:

Length 350 yards. Straight run. Posts 5 by 6, every 50 yards. Chestnut stobs (3 inches top diameter). 8 feet apart. 5 plain and 2 barbed wires.

	£	s.	d.
8 posts at 7s. 6d.	3	0	0
4 struts at 5s.	1	0	0
126 5 feet 6 inch stobs	7	10	0
750 yards B.W.	3	2	0
1,770 No. 8 plain wire	10	18	0
Staples, cartage, etc.	2	0	0
Labour	7	0	0
	£34	10	0

Cost per yard, say 2s.

A lighter fence of 5-foot posts, 3 by 3 inches top, can be erected for about 1s. 9d. per yard.

If protection against rabbits is required, 18-gauge 1¼-mesh netting, 42 inches high, must be added. The number of wires can be reduced to four. The top one can be barbed, the third can be used to attach the netting, and the fourth can be placed 18 inches from the ground to strengthen and steady the netting. The cost of such a fence on flat land would be about 3s. 6d. per yard. On

19. *A Leicestershire thorn fence seven years after laying.*

20. *Thorn fence trimmed annually for fifty years and here shown laid for the first time.*

21. *Maiden thorn fence in Leicestershire, laid for the first time.*

22. *Thorn fence laid and gapped.*

undulating ground it will cost more, as much time can be spent in bunching up or letting out the netting in order that it may fit the curves of the ground.

If rabbit netting alone is required a detailed specification will be found on page 100.

TOOLS USED FOR AGRICULTURAL HEDGING

The tools used by men working on agricultural hedges are as follows:

Hedging Gloves

Specially made of heavy leather. The left-hand one is used for handling brushwood, etc. It is therefore on the stiff side, and thick enough to prevent injury by thorns. The right-hand glove is more flexible, in order that the tool may be held satisfactorily.

Hedger's Axe

This is generally of light pattern, weighing about 4 pounds, with a handle 2 feet 9 inches to 3 feet in length.

Slasher

Slashers are of various patterns, the blade being in some cases pointed and in others with a slight hook. A favourite pattern curves slightly backwards, and is cut square at the end. Slashers used for trimming must be light in weight.

Pruning Saw

These are generally narrow, and taper off towards the end, so as to facilitate work among thick growth.

Billhook

This is perhaps the most important tool of all. Practically every county has its own pattern, and in some cases more than one pattern, according to the work it is required for. Billhooks are extensively used for general coppice work as well as for hedging, a typical example being the heavy hook used on the Welsh border for dealing with oak stems.

While as a general rule the hedge worker uses the type he prefers

E

it will be found that in one county or a collection of counties the patterns used resemble one another very closely. One of the most popular patterns in the Midlands is the 'Banbury' hook. This has a modified hook with a long point, the back of the blade having a straight cutting edge. There is practically no difference between this and the Leicestershire pattern.

Hedging tools must be kept extremely sharp. Blunt tools mean slow work and bad work. After being ground they should be finished on an oil or other whetstone.

HEDGEROW TIMBER

Few people will deny that the rural beauty of England would be ruined if the hedgerow timber, for so long the predominating feature of the countryside, were to disappear. On the other hand the farmer must be considered, for food production is, after all, far more important to the community than rural amenity.

The question of hedgerow timber has been a vexed one for very many years. Lord Kames, writing in the eighteenth century, considered that tree planting in hedgerows was 'a pernicious practice', that the trees ruined hedges by their shade, and checked their growth by competing with them for food. Other authorities wrote in much the same strain. Evelyn, while advocating the sowing of tree seeds in hedgerows, states that he is 'not ignorant of what is said against the scattering of these masts and seeds . . . which grown, overtop the subnascent hedge and prejudice it with their shade and drip'. But at that time wood for fuel was all-important, and hedgerow trees produced a type of timber useful for shipbuilding, so that in spite of these opinions the practice of planting trees in hedgerows continued to flourish.

Times have now changed, and the importance of hedgerow timber as a factor essential to the life of the community has largely diminished. Nevertheless, in spite of the disadvantages, there is something to be said in its favour.

The present-day objections to hedgerow timber are, as a matter of fact, very much what they always were. Shading of crops, with consequent loss of production, is the chief. Another is root competition. As regards hedges, tree-shading retards growth, and under the trees themselves the thorns, as they grow older and less vigorous, refuse to grow and gaps are formed.

On the other hand, trees act as a windbreak, and supply overhead shade which can be very useful to stockbreeders, especially at the hottest time of the day when the sun is directly overhead and the side shade of tall hedges or adjoining windscreens is of little or no value.

As regards damage to fences this is largely a question of management. If a tree is left to grow unchecked its branches will grow low down, and damage the hedge below. If, on the other hand, it is kept pruned up, sufficient light will be let in to allow of normal hedge growth. If the owner is anxious to grow trees and to keep a good hedge he can plant holly or hornbeam in the section close to the trees, and so avoid the result of interference with light, which affects a light-demanding species such as the thorn.

Trees in hedgerows are much exposed to wind, and cannot, therefore, be expected to produce the class of timber raised in plantations. But where they are properly looked after it is quite possible to produce trees that have a good timber value, although the number of species that can be used successfully is very limited.

It should be noted that these remarks refer solely to trees for the comparatively narrow hedges in use today, and not to the big hedge banks of the south-west or the 'cops' of the north of England, the trees of which are really narrow plantations rather than hedgerow timber.

Of the trees worth planting in hedges, oak is one of the best. It may be slow-growing but its shade is not intense, and being deep-rooted the tree does not interfere to any extent with cultivation. If shade only is required Turkey oak is faster growing, but its timber value is low. Elm is the typical hedgerow tree of the west of England. It grows well and fast, but spreads suckers which, if not checked, will damage a hedge considerably. Cases are found of neglected elm-planted hedgerows where it has been possible to make a good hedge by cutting back suckers which have killed out the original planting. Norway maple is quite a good hedge tree, grows straight and stands pruning well. Beech is bad. Its shade kills everything below it, its branches spread widely and its shape is usually poor. Ash is easily grown, but the shade is light and the roots travel great distances. Poplar is much the same as ash, but produces a far better quality timber. Conifers have little shade value, and as a rule do badly as isolated trees.

Whatever tree is planted it should be straight and clean for at least 5 feet. Trees that are found growing naturally should be gradually pruned, one third of the live branches being left untouched. Pruning must be done close to the stem so that no snags are left, and the tree must be encouraged to produce a straight leader. Otherwise it forms a bushy top that spoils the hedge and cannot produce a good timber tree.

Fruit Trees in Hedges

From the point of view of the tree itself there is no reason why on suitable soil fruit trees should not be planted in hedges. This practice is still carried out in certain parts of the country, especially in districts suitable for plums and damsons such as south-east Kent. Fruit-tree planting in hedges is a very old custom. Thus Norden, writing in 1610: 'I marvel men are not more forward in planting apples, pears and crab stocks in their hedges between the fields, and although some few may be lost a good mind will not grudge a wayfaring passenger taking for his refection and to qualify the heat of the day . . . the remnant will content the well-conditioned owner.' This advice might well be followed with advantage as far as the inner fields of a farm are concerned, but it is feared that the 'remnant' from trees planted near public roads would certainly not content most well-conditioned present-day owners!

Iron in Timber

Hedgerow trees should never be used as fence posts. Far too many trees are ruined by driving nails or staples into them. Merchants are suspicious of this class of tree for this reason, as a saw can be utterly ruined by striking a piece of iron. Every timber merchant has a collection of this type, ranging from ordinary nails to cow-chains and hinges. It may, therefore, be taken as a general rule that if a merchant finds nails, wire or staples in a tree he pays nothing for all the timber below them.

CHAPTER VI

FARM SHELTERBELTS-I

THE windbreak or shelterbelt is really a sort of a tall hedge, differing from the ordinary field hedge in its size and constitution. Windbreaks consist chiefly of trees planted in comparatively narrow strips, which have for their main object the provision of shelter to crops, stock and buildings by lessening the force, and consequently the action, of wind currents. By the provision of shelterbelts of this kind, evaporation of surface moisture is to some extent checked, and corn crops may be prevented from blowing flat. Cattle stand up to cold weather far better in sheltered fields, and appreciate the side shade afforded by tall windbreaks in summer. Another point in favour of windbreaks is the protection given against drifting snow. Snow has for many years been a problem that, as far as lowland farmers are concerned, has not given much trouble, but the winter of 1946–47 shows that it cannot be ruled out entirely.

The erosion of soil by wind may also be checked by shelterbelts. There seems to be an idea prevalent that this problem does not arise in Great Britain. While trouble of this kind is not likely to occur on the same scale as in the United States it nevertheless does exist in this country, especially on the light soils of Lincolnshire and East Anglia. In parts of North and West Norfolk it is possible to find top soil forming mounds on the leeward sides of fields, and filling up ditches. Sugarbeet seedlings have been blown out of the ground, and sowings of light seeds completely ruined. The soils most affected are the fen soils and the light soils, especially those over marl.

In Jersey, the increase in tomato cultivation has led to the wholesale cutting back or removal of hedges and trees in order to let in as much light as possible. As a result wind erosion, once unheard of, is now a problem which may have a serious effect on the small, highly rented farms of the island. This is a proof of the value of the windscreen to light, highly cultivated soils. Fifty years ago the hedges and hedgerow trees were one of the island's most prominent features. Now, with a large proportion of the hedges cut hard or removed, and the rows of hedgerow trees either felled or cut back to unsightly poles, the wind can work unchecked, and the situation is such that serious action is now proposed by the local authorities to try to remedy the damage.

On light soils the surface of which dries out to powder, the provision of shelterbelts will greatly lessen the danger of soil loss by windblow, and if this loss of soil and soil fertility is set against the cost of planting and establishing wind barriers it will generally prove a satisfactory investment.

On the hill farms of Great Britain carefully sited belts should vastly increase the amount of high ground that can be used for summer feeding. Much of such protected land is also available for wintering purposes. If the area and grazing quality of the higher lands were increased lower grounds could be reserved for hay crops for winter use. In far too many cases stock has to be fed on these areas during the summer owing to lack of keep at higher altitudes.

The planting of screens on hill farms is a very different problem from the same work in the lowlands. In the lowlands the problem is comparatively simple, as conditions do not vary greatly, and whatever the soil, it is not difficult to find species of tree and shrub that will grow satisfactorily if properly 'done'. Except perhaps for coast planting, exposure is not as a rule severe. On the hills the matter is more complex. Exposure is often serious, which means that the choice of trees is restricted. Soil conditions are often far from satisfactory, and planting without careful forethought may result in a screen that has very little value. Valleys have a way of 'siphoning' the wind so that it rushes up or down in a most disconcerting manner. At one end or the other the currents may become so confused that it is extremely difficult to determine the best site to plant. In hill country, especially where the soil is inclined to be heavy, a soil 'pan' is often present, and must be broken thoroughly if satisfactory growth is to be obtained.

Screen planting on high-lying land has, therefore, a technique of its own which is not yet fully developed, and afforestation on high land now being carried out by the Forestry Commission should eventually provide information most valuable to the planter of windbreaks.

While it is universally admitted that on the whole windbreaks are useful and desirable, there are, of course, certain disadvantages attached to them. Certain claims occasionally made in their favour are also either negligible in value or without foundation. One argument against windbreaks is that they delay crop ripening by side shading. The degree of shading depends on the siting of the screen and on its constitution. If the screen is on the north side shading is negligible, but this siting is of course rare, south-west or north-east planting being more usual in order to check the prevailing winds. Overhead shade and drip can be dealt with by cutting back, or by planting trees which do not naturally throw out wide-spreading lateral branches.

Another objection is root competition. The trees of the windbreak will tend to spread their roots into the field in search of moisture and food, the latter being chiefly nitrogen. Loss of moisture is especially likely to affect root crops on the lighter soils. For this reason deep-rooting trees should be planted on such soils whenever possible. Such trees as poplar should be avoided, as these not only require much water, but the roots interfere with cultivation. Against this it may be argued that what is lost on the swings is gained on the roundabouts, i.e. that the loss by shading, etc., is more than counterbalanced by crop improvements in other parts of the field due to the presence of the belts.

It is occasionally suggested that the presence of shelterbelts helps to increase the rainfall. This appears extremely improbable, at any rate as far as Great Britain is concerned. It is also suggested that the presence of shelterbelts reduces evaporation from the soil, and so helps to conserve moisture. This may be true as far as normal wet-dry conditions are concerned, but when drought occurs the windbreak appears to have little or no effect as a preventive of 'drying out'. Every farmer and gardener knows that although soil moisture can be conserved to some extent by mechanical or hand cultivation, a point may be reached where such action becomes ineffective. It is the same with wind screens.

To state categorically that windbreaks are of no value to the

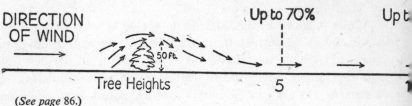

REDUCTION

DIRECTION
OF WIND

Up to 70%   Up t

50 ft.

Tree Heights   5

(See page 86.)

arable farmer in Britain would be incorrect. There is no doubt
that in certain cases and in certain conditions they can be of
considerable use, especially on large farms in comparatively
flat districts. As far as stock is concerned the advantages far
outweigh the disadvantages.

Finally, it must not be forgotten that the value of a windbreak,
unlike that of implements, appreciates rather than depreciates,
and that the initial cost must be spread over its effective life, which
should be at least fifty years.

It has already been stated that one of the most important
reasons for the planting of screen or break is to provide shelter
against wind. That screens do afford shelter is obvious to anyone
standing on the lee side of one of them when the wind is blowing.
It is also obvious to anyone walking against the wind towards
a screen that the strength of the wind diminishes as the screen is
approached. The question that arises out of this is the actual
value of the planting for practical purposes. If this can be ascertained, however roughly, it is possible to get a guide as to the
amount of protection supplied by a screen of a particular height,
or conversely the height of screen or hedge that will afford protection to a given area.

The efficiency of a windbreak or hedge depends on several
factors. Its object as a unit is to divert wind currents as far as
possible from the area to be protected, or at least to break up
the currents in such a way that the original force is lessened.

Wind currents, on meeting a solid obstacle such as a wall, rise
over or go around it. In the case of a belt of trees they also go
through, the force of penetration depending on the constitution
of the belt. The check thus imposed, combined with the 'carry
over' of the currents above the top of the belt, combine to produce

WIND VELOCITY

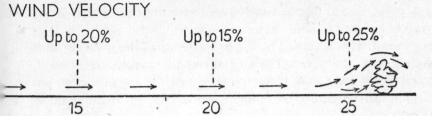

—at any rate in the case of dense belts—a comparatively calm zone immediately behind the trees.

Windflow round the sides of a belt usually exceeds the force of the main currents, as anyone knows who has tried to grow trees near the sides of tall, isolated buildings. It also works inwards. For this reason the area protected by a belt of trees on one side only, gradually assumes a triangular shape, so that if maximum protection for a single square field is required the wind belt must be at least twice as long as the field is wide.

The ideal windbreak for Great Britain's comparatively small areas will have more than one side, and it is sometimes possible to link it with tall hedgerows or woods for this purpose. An angled windbreak may have to be planted in some cases where the use of a long line is impossible, owing, for example, to difference in ownership of the land.

Where wide fields are to be protected, parallel belts can be planted. To obtain maximum depth protection these should be spaced at intervals not exceeding twenty-five times the ultimate height of the belts ; i.e. for 50-foot belts the distance between belts would be about a quarter of a mile.

The next point to consider is the maximum depth of protection that may be expected, and the degree of protection that may be afforded at various distances to leeward of the screen. A fairly dense belt, that is to say one in which the lower part is effectively filled up with shrubs or low-growing trees, will of course give better results than the more open types. With dense screens the force of the wind near the belt may be cut down by as much as 75 per cent. A screen 40 feet in height may cut the force of a 35 m.p.h. wind by 20 per cent. at a distance of 200 yards, thus reducing the wind at this point from a strong wind to a fresh breeze.

A point that is not generally realized is that the force of the wind is lessened to some extent on the windward side as well as to leeward. This is caused by the breaking up of the wind currents as they strike the screen. The area affected is comparatively small, possibly not more than twice the height of the actual screen, but close in it may reduce the strength of the wind by anything up to 25 per cent.

C. C. Bates states[1] that 'the effects of all windbreaks[2] are similar at distances measured roughly in equal multiples of the height of the trees, so that tree height can be used as the unit of horizontal distance measure in comparisons of different situations'. The degree of wind force at, say, 250 feet from a belt 50 feet high is, therefore, described as being '5 heights' from the belt.

Figures showing such effects are not very numerous, but as far as can be ascertained average effect is roughly as follows. It is expressed as reduction in wind velocity, and refers to fairly dense screens well closed in from ground-level upwards.

Number of tree heights from belt.	Approximate percentage reduction in wind velocity.
2	75
5	66
10	50
15	20
20	15
30	10

So that with a belt 50 feet high the force of a 30 m.p.h. wind may be cut down to 15 m.p.h. at 10 heights (500 feet).

If the belt was only 25 feet high the 15 m.p.h. zone would probably be found about 250 feet from the belt (10 heights).

Some protective effect will generally be found to exist at over 30 heights, but for practical purposes this distance may be taken as the limit, although with very thick, well-bottomed screens the degree of protection related to screen height may extend slightly farther out.

[1] 'The Windbreak as a Farm Asset'. *Farmers' Bulletin, No. 1405.* U.S. Department of Agriculture.
[2] Presumably of similar density.

Thin screens which are very open at the bottom, especially those composed of poplar and Scots pine, give little protection against ground draught. With belts of this type the maximum reduction in wind velocity is often not more than 20 per cent. at any point behind the screen, so that their value as screens is lost until ground planting on one side or the other is carried out. In such cases there is often no appreciable reduction in wind velocity near the trees. Wind forces its way through at ground-level, with a tendency to rise upwards. The zone of maximum protection may therefore be sited at any distance up to 5 heights from the screen.

That stock have realized this is shown by the fact that cattle seldom congregate under the lee of a thin, poorly furnished wind-break, but are generally found lying some distance away from it.

As far as siting is concerned this, in Great Britain, is generally controlled by the direction of the prevailing wind. The chief winds from which protection is required are from the south-west and north-east. The south-west winds are, as a rule, the most destruc-tive, and those from the north-east the coldest.

With regard to snow, the actual size and position of the planting area may be important, especially where farm roads and buildings are concerned. In such cases belts 8 to 10 lines wide are more efficient than belts of 2 or 3 lines. With the wider belt the snow tends to drift on the windward side and among the trees. With the narrow planting, snow blows through the trees, and velocity being checked the drift forms on the far side. Thin belts planted close to a farm road, especially if a sunken one, should, therefore, be sited on the west side of the road rather than on the east.

Extensive protection on the southern side of a field is not desirable, as it interferes with the light and heat required by crops. Nor is it particularly desirable for stock, as it provides a minimum of shade in the summer.

The siting of a windbreak should, therefore, be based on what it is actually required for, and the season when the value of the screen can be utilized to the maximum. As has already been mentioned the presence of high land may produce 'funnelling' from a direction quite different from that of ordinary winds. It is, therefore, quite impossible to lay down any definite rules for siting, which must depend on local conditions and requirements. On high land individual trees, even in comparatively sheltered positions, will often help to indicate the direction of 'local draughts' by their shape.

The Constitution of Farm Windbreaks

It is generally considered that the efficiency of a farm windbreak depends on its width, but very wide windbreaks, amounting to plantations, are apt to interfere with their own object. If the screen is very wide the wind currents tend to level out as they cross the trees, so that when the area to be protected is reached the current pours down close behind the screen, instead of some distance beyond it.

As has already been shown the most valuable windbreak is the highest, provided always that it is well furnished to ground-level. A 30-foot-wide planting, with low-branched trees, and carefully sited bushes or shrubs, will do the work required as efficiently as one twice its width with an open bottom, is cheaper to establish, and takes up less land.

Very narrow plantings of two or three rows of trees are far better than nothing, and afford a certain amount of protection. They are, however, very difficult to keep thick at ground-level, and the only really satisfactory way to improve them is to plant additional lines of low-growing trees or bushes, preferably on the sheltered side.

Shelterbelts planted solely for the purpose of windbreaks should be from 30 to 60 feet wide, to be really effective. If they are planted with the idea of obtaining fencing and other material from the thinnings, they should be at least four times this width.

Trees planted as windbreaks must be planted closely, to give early protection and to assist height growth. Close planting means planting at intervals of 4 to 5 feet, although it is a good thing to widen the intervals to about 8 feet on the exposed edge. This gives more room for root formation, which helps to steady the outer lines of trees. If artificial shelter can be obtained it will be invaluable, even if only a few feet high. Old walls, hedges, banks or even mounds thrown up by a bulldozer will help the trees to establish themselves far more quickly than when completely exposed.

As regards the composition of windbreaks most people seem to prefer conifers, as providing the maximum shelter throughout the year. Hardwoods, however, can make efficient screens. A mixture of the two is quite sound, and the leaves of the hardwoods will provide humus for soil improvement. The value of a line or two of hardwoods on the exposed side can be very great, as these trees take the force of the wind and break it up before the main wall of evergreens is reached. Probably the most useful species of hardwood for this purpose, especially at the higher altitudes, is sycamore. It is very hardy and wind-resisting, and grows satisfactorily on most soils, including limestones, shales and coal measures. On acid moorland boundary soil, where it may be planted to save more valuable land, its growth is quite satisfactory for sheltering purposes. Its appearance is often ugly, misshapen and gaunt, but the small branches and twigs it throws out into the teeth of the wind do their work efficiently.

Another tree of considerable value at high altitudes is the mountain ash, which makes an excellent outer barrier at 1,000 feet and over. At lower altitudes, especially on clay loams, white poplar is most useful, and stands wind very well. If kept low by cutting, the branches thicken up, and when the leaf is on there is no better screen for the purpose of preventing ground draught. Most conifers as they grow up tend to lose lower branches, so that some type of low cover is necessary. This can be provided by planting low-growing trees or shrubs on the inside and outside edges of the screen, of which elder, thorn, privet and snowberry are perhaps the hardiest and best. A thorn hedge planted fairly widely (18 inches to 2 feet apart) and allowed to grow up makes an effective draught excluder, but unless topped occasionally is liable to be broken down by snow. By keeping it below 6 feet in height there is a better chance of a good bottom.

As regards conifers the trees obtainable today for this purpose are Scots and Corsican pines, and spruce. Two other excellent trees for shelter work are Austrian and mountain pine. The former, with a naturally rough and spreading crown, is a first-class shelter tree at low elevations. The mountain pine is spreading and thick. It holds its branches almost to ground-level so that, used as a backing to other species such as Corsican, a thick screen is maintained, and ground draughts can be prevented. Unfortunately at the present time (1951) neither Austrian nor mountain pine is available in quantity, but Austrian pine will be obtainable in quantity in two or three years' time. Corsican pine is one of the best shelter trees, but owing to its poor root system when young it is a bad transplanter, and is apt to blow on soft ground, where, incidentally, it should never be planted. It has made good screens up to 1,300 feet and more in Wales, but in Scotland it is not so successful, owing possibly to the colder climate. It is, perhaps, the best conifer for planting on chalk or limestone soils. On such soils beech can often be usefully added.

Scots pine is suitable for screen work, but is best used with broad-leaved trees on the outsides, as narrow belts quickly lose their lower branches and allow the wind to come through at ground-level. A most successful high elevation screen using Scots pine has been planted as follows:

2 rows sycamore   6 feet apart
4 rows Scots pine   4 feet 6 inches apart

Locality: N. Wales. Height 1,250 feet. Planting fully exposed to S.W. and W. Soil: loam over slaty rock.

On damp or peaty land, especially at high elevations, Sitka spruce appears the obvious choice. It is more wind-firm than Norway spruce, and stands peaty heathery conditions far better. It is best planted at 6-foot intervals, and should have a protective outside belt of mountain ash or sycamore if the soil permits. Good soil is not needed for such trees, in fact is a handicap, as what is required in this case is rough form and comparatively slow growth. On poorer soils where growth is not likely to be rapid Sitka spruce can be mixed with Scots to advantage.

Narrow Belts

For single- or two-line belts at the lower elevations Lombardy poplar planted at 6- to 8-foot intervals is generally a good choice. Even when very tall this tree holds its branches well down, making the best single screen possible, at any rate as far as deciduous trees are concerned. Black poplar can be used in the same way, but as it approaches middle age the stem branches tend to disappear.[1] It can of course be topped, but, especially when it is planted closely, the new branches tend to break off. Lombardy poplar stands topping quite well, forming what is really a very high hedge. It can be seen cut in this way making excellent shelter for Kentish hop gardens.

Pines can be used for single- or double-line work, but unless widely planted soon lose their lower branches. Put in on an old hedge line where there are still overgrown thorns standing; or better still, planted behind an old overgrown hedge Corsican or Austrian pine can produce quite good sheltering effects. In fact Austrian makes the best single line windbreak of any pine.

Old wide banks can be patched up with trees, but when doing this the degree of demand for light must not be forgotten. It is, therefore, no use planting pines in the shade of other trees. Spruce will stand slight shading; beech, hornbeam and holly will stand even more. Yew is the best of all, but should never be used in farm windbreaks, as it is poisonous to stock.

At medium elevations it is possible to plant closely about 4 feet apart, with the idea of getting a certain number of poles for farm use. In such cases common larch can be tried alternately with other more heavily leafed conifers. Larch prunes other species very badly, and is easily pruned by them, and a mixture will provide clean larch and rough other species. The larch can come out and leave the rougher branched trees to make the screen—but, it should be added, only where the site is a good one, and never on old ploughland or in frosty places. In regions of heavy rainfall Japanese larch is a better tree.

Hardwood Belts

In some cases deciduous trees may be required, and excellent windbreaks can be made of them, although it is sound practice to add a certain number of coniferous trees to thicken them up.

For such plantings, sycamore and Norway maple are good.

[1] This variety and certain others can be planted as temporary windbreaks to be felled for timber when mature. If not less than 200 are planted on any one estate in one season they become eligible for a Government grant of 2s. per tree. These trees must be planted in one or two lines only and must be at least 18 feet apart.

Mountain ash and whitebeam grow at high elevations. Ash and elm can be used, while on heavy soils hornbeam, although slow-growing, is nevertheless a good type of shelter tree, as it is hardy and stands overshade. Beech can be used almost anywhere, and even at 1,000 feet will make a good protective unit, although as a timber tree it will be of little or no value. Poplars, apart from *P. alba* and Lombardy poplars, should be avoided. They may grow quickly, but after the first twenty-five years or so their value for shelter purposes is practically nil, and they stand up to wind very badly. Willow on the other hand is a good wind resister, and is well worth including in damp sites.

If a line or two of conifers is to be added, and this practice is strongly recommended, Corsican or Austrian pine are perhaps the best except on dry sands at low or medium elevation, where Scots pine is probably the most suitable species to use.

23. *Scots pine windbreak at Elveden, Suffolk.*

24. *Thorn windscreen on a hop farm at Bodiam, Sussex.*

93

25. *'Fenblow', Cambridgeshire.*

26. *Top-soil piled up by the wind at Thetford, Norfolk.*

CHAPTER VII

FARM SHELTERBELTS-II

PLANTS for shelterbelts must be of good quality, as from
the nature of their situation they must be able to look after
themselves from the beginning. The most important thing is
the root, which should be comparatively heavy, and well furnished
with fibre. Heavy roots should not, however, be expected with
Corsican pine, which is notoriously deficient in this respect. The
ideal plant is short and stocky. Big plants should not be used, as,
apart from the fact that the proportion of root to stem is usually
too low, they are likely to be rocked by wind, and so take some
time to establish themselves. Small plants establish themselves
more quickly, and start growing sooner, with the result that
plants put in at twice the size are frequently soon surpassed in
height.

Plants lifted from adjoining woodlands are always useless, as
their roots are not sufficiently developed to stand the change of
site, and their age is usually unknown. Nursery-grown transplants should always be used; short, stout three-year-old trees
transplanted at least once in the nursery being ideal for the
purpose.

Treatment Before Planting

Tree roots soon dry out if exposed to the atmosphere, especially
if there is a cold wind blowing. After being unpacked the plants
should, therefore, be placed in shallow trenches with their roots
well covered with soil, the plants being placed in thin rows one
or two plants thick to avoid the possibility of heating. When
lifted for planting they should be placed in a big haversack, or
better still in a bucket or other container, in the bottom of which
is a thin mixture of soil and water. The importance of such
protection is still not sufficiently realized, and often failure and
disappointment result from its neglect.

Preparation of the Ground for Planting

Treatment will vary according to the condition of the surface, but as this will generally be in grass or arable it should not present much difficulty. Waste land with heather and gorse will also be found. This again does not present much difficulty, provided always that the possibility of a 'pan' is realized and suitable action taken. 'Pan', which is a hard, impermeable layer of soil, is formed on acid soils by the leaching down of iron salts from the surface layer. It may be a few inches below the surface, and it may be 1 inch or several inches in thickness. It interferes with the movement of water in the soil, both downwards and upwards. Deepset 'pan' can be broken up by special ploughs of a heavy type, but this is expensive. Fortunately it is possible to raise quite satisfactory windbreaks over deepset pan, as this does not, as a rule, interfere very much with growth, especially if shallow-rooted species can be used. Shallow pan, within 12 inches of the surface, can usually be broken through by hand, or by plough. Pan is a problem which often has to be faced on flat land at high elevations.

Peat is another problem, and this has a special technique of its own, which is dealt with on page 98.

Ordinary arable land presents little difficulty as a rule, as the soil is usually well broken up and weed-free. Land that has been down to arable for many years may have a 'plough pan', caused by the repeated pressure of the plough at a certain depth. This, however, seldom seems to affect growth, except in the case of larch.

Grassland is not quite so simple to deal with. Planting into holes cut in the turf can be and is often done, but it is not always satisfactory, as there is considerable competition with the grass roots for food and moisture, which leads to slowness in establishment and often, especially in dry summers, to quite a number of deaths. Simple ploughing up is useless where there is much twitch grass, as this comes back through the furrow slice and the situation is no better than it was before. The ideal method is to plough up the strip cultivate it and take off a crop such as winter oats. The ground will then be in a condition in which to set out small, well-rooted plants, which can take advantage of the broken turf, and which, having no competition from grass weeds, can get away quickly. In cases where it is not practicable to take off a crop, pre-cultivation is always useful. If the ground is broken up in this way, planting is easier, root run is helped, and growth is far better.

On light, dry soils it is also possible to plough out furrows at the required planting distance and then set the plants in the furrow, which helps to shelter them and concentrates the moisture in the places where it can be used to the best advantage. At higher altitudes, especially where the rainfall is heavy, grass root competition is not desirable, and on such soils planting direct into inverted turves produces results which are usually more satisfactory than planting on the flat.

Method of Planting

For ordinary areas planting in pits is undoubtedly the best method to use for windbreaks. With a pit of, say, 10 by 10 inches, the root is spread out and can grow away in all directions. There are other methods set out in detail in all good forestry textbooks, but their chief advantage is speed, which when working on windbreaks is not a matter of great importance. Pit planting is done in exactly the same way as shrub planting. The two main things to remember are to put the strongest roots to the wind, and *to tread them in hard after the soil has been put back*. This prevents swaying and water-logging. Treading should be done with the heel, preferably of a leather boot. It has been very truly said that next to the rabbit the forester's greatest enemy is the rubber boot! But a leather heel must be used with care, to avoid bark damage.

There are various other methods of planting, 'notching' being the most usual. These, however, are purely forestry methods which are not recommended for screen planting. On rocky or easy-working soils modified pit planting, using a wide mattock, is often useful. One point on pit planting is worth remembering. It is sometimes suggested that when planting in heavy soils it is a good practice to dig the hole some time before planting. This is a mistake. In the majority of cases when the time for planting comes the holes will be found half-full of water, and the earth that has been dug out will have almost entirely disappeared. Apart from this the sides of the hole often 'set' in such a way that the rootlets cannot penetrate, and the result is more or less the same as planting in a small pot.

When planting, the trees should be set in quincunx, that is to say in staggered lines.

Turf planting is the standard method of planting on peaty soil and for wet, grassy areas. Trees do not grow satisfactorily in soils which are constantly wet, and either die or take a long time to establish themselves. Turf planting lifts the tree above the wet level. For windbreak work wet areas should be avoided as far as possible, as there is always risk of windblow, but there may be cases where planting on such soil is unavoidable. Turf planting is easy to carry out in theory, but its satisfactory execution depends very much on the correct assessment of local conditions. Farmers and estate owners considering this would, therefore, be well advised to apply to the local Conservator of the Forestry Commission for assistance in procedure.

Turf planting is so called because instead of planting at normal soil-level the plants are set into inverted turves cut from the area, usually from turf strips taken out in the direction that will most assist drainage. On very wet areas open drains must be cut, as if the ground is waterlogged within, say, 2 feet of the surface growth will suffer. Turves must be turned over and laid grass side down as soon as they are cut. They are usually 15 inches square and about 6 inches thick, but soon decrease in thickness as they dry out. They should be given a month or six weeks to settle before actual planting takes place. Planting is done by cutting a slit in the turf from the edge to the centre in the half away from the prevailing wind. The plant is then slipped into the cut, care being taken to see that the roots are properly spread out below the turf. The turf then falls back with the root sandwiched between the grassy side of the turf and the natural surface of the planting area, and the cut is trodden down hard to close it. The fact that part of the stem may be covered does not matter, as the shrinkage of the turf will eventually free it. Turfing can also be done by ploughing out two deep furrows and planting into the upturned slices. On dry sites planting should be done at the bottom or on the edge of the furrow.

Such soils as these are generally only suited to spruce, and
Sitka spruce should be used, as it is much more windfirm than the
ordinary common spruce. This is a case where plants must be
small and stout, and if the soil is very poor should be assisted by
the application of a handful of basic slag at the time of planting.
This is the only type of planting where the application of artificial
manure appears worth while.

Cost of Establishment

The cost of planting and establishing windbreaks naturally
depends on local conditions, especially on such things as the type
of soil, accessibility, the amount of preliminary work that is
necessary, and the kind of plants.

In ordinary conditions the cost of a six-row belt should be
much as follows, the length of the windbelt being taken as 100
yards, interval between plants 4 feet 6 inches, or say 70 plants
to the line. It would be best to purchase 80 plants per line in order
to allow for a few trees not being up to the requisite standard.

For a six-row belt four rows of pine with a row of hardwoods
on the outer sides might be used, at a cost of about £8 0s. 0d. per
100 yards for plants, planting and pre-cultivation.

In too many cases protection against rabbits is essential.
Netting is a very expensive business, especially where areas are
long and narrow. If, however, rabbits are not numerous, or can
be kept well down, planting without netting is worth considering,
as the initial saving is so great. But every tree killed or badly
damaged must be replaced, at any rate for the first three or four
years.

It must, however, be remembered that rabbits may be scarce in
one season and numerous in another, and that a plantation may
go through two mild winters undamaged, and be ruined by rabbits
if the next winter happens to be exceptionally severe. One way of
lessening cost is to remove the fencing for use elsewhere after
four or five years if there are no signs of rabbits.

Protection against stock is absolutely necessary. Cattle do
damage by treading down small plants, but as far as damage by
eating goes they do not compare with sheep, who will eat every
leaf off. For protection against heavy cattle a stock-rabbit fence

similar to that described in Chapter V is as cheap and efficient as any.

The cost of a rabbit-proof fence per chain will be much as follows (straining posts set at corners and 100-yard intervals; netting dug in to a depth of 6 inches):

	£	s.	d.
22 yards 42-inch 1¼-mesh 18-gauge netting .	1	12	0
8 stakes, 5 feet 6 inches, 3-inch top . .		8	0
23 yards barbed top-wire		2	0
23 yards No. 8 galvanized plain wire . .		2	0
Proportion of strainers and struts . .		3	0
Staples and tie-wire, etc.		1	0
Labour		10	0
	£2	18	0

This is equivalent to 2s. 7½d. per yard or, say, with haulage and supervision 2s. 9d. per yard.

Actually the best protection against rabbits is not to have any !

Where land is rabbit-free and netting can be dispensed with, the cost, compared with the benefit obtained, appears reasonable. Unfortunately there are comparatively few areas that can be safely considered as rabbit-free, and in such cases the necessity for wiring may treble the cost. A six-row belt 350 yards in length may, therefore, cost anything up to £130 0s. 0d. inclusive of a certain amount of after-care.

As the provision of shelterbelts is classed as essential capital expenditure the cost can be set against income-tax, and this, plus the value of such poles as are removed when thinning, might reduce the actual expenditure to about £65 0s. 0d.

Such a belt should provide useful protection for some 12 acres, or even more where cattle are concerned, as animals often range over more than one field.

The capital cost per acre receiving protection is therefore about £6 0s. 0d.

The period of maximum protection may be reasonably set at about fifty years, so that the cost per acre protected per annum is approximately 2s. 5d.

It may not be necessary to plant shelterbelts round every field. A large farm might have only one or two carefully sited belts up to which the cattle might work in bad weather, and in such cases the rent charge for protection against wind would be practically nominal.

The argument against belt planting is largely based on finance, as, apart from the fact that tax rebate can only be recovered over a series of years, farmers are already faced with heavy commitments for fixed equipment demanded by the Agriculture Act. Also, where 'soil blow' is concerned, the fact that this can take place when the wind is in any quarter means that the single shelterbelt is not wholly effective.

But if the long view is taken there seems little doubt that in certain parts of the country, notably on hill farms, on the lighter soils of East Anglia, and on the wind-swept downs of the southwest, the shelterbelt will eventually prove to be an essential factor in the satisfactory upkeep of the farm.

After-care

Transplants, especially conifers that carry their foliage all the year round, are liable to be swayed about by the wind. If this is continuous an open pocket will be formed between stem and soil, which may lead to stem rot or drying out. Plants should, therefore, be inspected at intervals during the first year or two and trodden back hard. All dead or dying trees must be replaced.

Weeding may be necessary, especially on the better soils. There is no need to clear all the ordinary weeds, such as grass, thistles, fireweed or foxgloves, completely off the area. These often supply useful shelter to young trees, particularly during hot summers. All that is required is to chop round the trees with a hoe and give them room to 'see the sky'. Care should be taken, however, as winter approaches to make certain that ground vegetation is not tall enough to be pushed on top of the trees by the weight of snow.

Thin low growths of bracken, often seen in disused grassland, make a good summer shelter, but high bracken must be got rid of by annual cuttings, preferably in June before the fronds have uncurled. Heather must be cut if it starts to crowd the transplants.

On old agricultural land a long windbreak can be easily and quickly dealt with by the Allan Motor Scythe.

Once the leading shoots are well up over the weeds little attention is required in the way of weeding, except for such things as honeysuckle and other climbers.

Thinning Shelterbelts

When thinning shelterbelts the main object, that of providing a barrier against wind, must always be borne in mind. In the early stages thinning should start just before the lower branches of a tree approach those of its neighbour very closely. In the ideal plantation, in which every tree grows alike, the solution is fairly simple, as all that has to be done is to take out alternate trees. Planting is often done on this basis, pine being planted alternately with larch at intervals of 5 feet. The larch is all cut out and the pine is left at 10-foot intervals to form the screen. Unfortunately growth is not always 'according to Cocker', and the owner quite frequently finds places where the pine has not grown well, and if the larch is taken out there will be nasty gaps. With hardwoods, what is required is a minimum of stem and a maximum of crown, the reverse in fact of what is termed 'good sylviculture'. Hardwoods interfering with softwoods or better hardwoods can be coppiced back, and the new shoots will help to give ground shelter. Beech, however, coppices badly and slowly, especially under the shade of other trees. Dead, dying and diseased trees should always be removed. On most soils a final distance of 10 feet or so apart will provide a satisfactory barrier that only requires an occasional tree taken out. With very wide belts of 3 chains and up, thinning can be more severe, as there is greater margin for error. Also the windward half can be treated differently from the leeward half. But as in ordinary forestry the cardinal rule for thinning holds good, i.e. never cut a tree without a perfectly good reason for doing so.

Windscreens for Orchards

Tree plantings on orchard boundaries are at times very useful, as they help to prevent damage by cold, cutting winds. They prevent breakage of branches, especially where the fruit crop is heavy. And as bees prefer to work in calm weather a reduction of wind force assists pollination.

For orchards it is generally considered that coniferous screens are better than those composed of deciduous trees, as they give better shelter, and are not liable to act as secondary hosts for certain diseases attacking fruit trees, such as 'Silver Leaf', which is sometimes the case with broadleaved varieties.

Screens, especially tall screens, should not be planted too close to the orchard, as a region of unusual calm such as may be expected close up to a tall screen may encourage frost damage. Also the orchard trees may be affected by root competition from the trees forming the screen. For this reason it is as well to keep the screen at least 35 feet from the main fruit planting.

If conifers are used for screening, pyramidal trees should be used to economize space. Spruce is perhaps the cheapest and best tree to use for this purpose. A few hardwoods will strengthen the screen, and of these Norway maple should prove very satisfactory. For a quick screen C. macrocarpa planted about 4 to 5 feet apart can be used. Small plants, preferably from pots, are best.

The configuration of the area is sometimes important, as, if ignored, a screen may be placed in such a position that the downward cold air-flow is checked, and damage by frost is the result.

Stock Shelter in Fields

A type of planting which is worth considering where shelterbelts are not required is that of small plantings designed to provide not only shelter for stock but also a certain amount of farm timber. Ordinary belts seldom produce poles or timber of value, as they are too narrow to provide the necessary shelter from the adjoining trees. Plantings such as these should be as large as possible if timber is required, especially if conifers are being used. They should not be less than 66 feet through at the thinnest point. The ideal shape of such plantings would be more or less oval, with concave bends so designed as to give the maximum shelter against north-east and south-west winds. Square plantings are cheaper to fence, and protection is given by the plantation sides, but the former type looks more natural, and the bays are certainly warmer in the winter.

Planting naturally depends on the soil; Scots pine on dry soil, Corsican pine on chalks or medium clays, and spruce on heavy soils. Larch can be used on medium soils, to come out in the early stages as poles. Japanese larch should, however, not be used, unless planted in pure groups of about ten trees, as its growth and comparatively heavy canopy of leaves do not fit it for mixing purposes. Beech is always useful, and can be either scattered or planted around the edges. Ash can be added, and if it is taken out as poles when thinning is being done the stump will shoot again, and help to provide ground shelter.

The best planting distance is 5 feet. This will allow the larch to come out, and leave the main crop standing 10 feet apart, with plenty of low branches which the larch will not have shaded off and killed. A rough thorn hedge will make the plantation even more efficient from the stock protection point of view.

CHAPTER VIII

COAST SCREENS AND SHELTERBELTS

WHILE the climate of Great Britain as a whole is affected by the fact that the country is surrounded by the sea there is, as far as vegetation is concerned, a considerable difference between coast and inland areas. Generally speaking the coast on the west, being closer to the Atlantic, has a comparatively mild winter and a greater rainfall than that of the eastern side. As might be expected the south coast varies between the two extremes, being mildest in the west with a gradual decrease as the east coast is approached. Mildness of climate in the west is due to the warm south-westerly wind. This wind, coming over the Atlantic, is naturally moisture-laden, and, striking the mountains and highlands of the west, produces the comparatively heavy rainfall which is found in the greater part of the western coast areas. On the east coast the climate is drier and colder, and there are many days of cold and cutting winds, especially from the north-east.

On the west and south-western coasts the winters are usually so mild, and the climate as a whole so warm, that provided the planting site is adequately protected from wind, many sub-tropical plants can be successfully grown. Coast planting needs adequate protection from wind at all times and everywhere, not only for sub-tropical trees but also for ordinary trees and shrubs, and without such protection the planting scheme has too often failed before it is planted.

The effect of wind can be grasped by studying the appearance of any wood or group of trees near the edge of the sea. The outer side will be battered, rough and stunted, and its shape will curve away from the wind. The trees farther in will be taller and better shaped. This improvement will continue until, if the group is sufficiently wide, normal growth and appearance is obtained. Shelterbelts for coast gardens should be planted with this idea in mind, strong, hardy, wind-resisting trees and shrubs on the exposed side changing gradually inwards to the more valuable species.

Trees suitable for coast shelterbelts will naturally vary according to soil conditions and climate. What will grow in Cornwall may not suit East Kent, and what will suit East Kent may not be satisfactory on the Yorkshire coast.

Many of the deciduous trees already recommended for farm shelterbelts will be found useful, especially for the windward sides. White poplar, for example, is extremely hardy, does not seem to mind spray, and grows quite well in sandy soils. Its suckering power in such soils is very marked, and this property makes it all the more valuable. Here again it should be kept lopped at a height of 6 to 8 feet, to make a thick screen low down and so block out ground draughts. Elm is a useful tree for this purpose. It gets battered and unshapely, but makes a good screen tree. Sycamore is even better, and for really exposed situations is perhaps the best deciduous tree for coast planting where the belt is wide.

Other deciduous trees recommended for screens are, willows, whitebeam, mountain ash, holm oak, whitethorn, aspen, black poplar.

Good 'second line' trees are Norway maple, holly, birch, grey alder, beech, Turkey oak.

Among conifers which are most valuable for the exposed side of a plantation Austrian pine is undoubtedly one of the best. It thrives near the sea and its rough, heavily branched habit makes it a first-class shelter tree. Its close relation, the Corsican pine, also grows very well near the sea, but its habit is straight, and its branches are not so heavy, nor do they hang on as long as Austrian pine. This pine is best used as a 'backbone' inside the belt, but can be used outside if Austrian pine is not available.

The Maritime pine (*P. Pinaster*) is a first-class seaside tree, a quick grower that thrives in the sandiest of soil. This is the pine that helped to make Bournemouth famous. The Remarkable pine (*P. radiata*) is another tree that grows extremely well by the sea. Neither of these trees stands severe cold, but they are worth planting in the south and west. At the present time (1951) they are difficult, if not impossible, to obtain in quantity.

The Scots pine is often planted by the sea, but it does not stand wind and spray well. Given a little protection such as can be found in the middle of a belt it will do well, and being cheap will help to keep down planting costs.

No conifer, in fact no tree of any kind, grows better near the sea than the Monterey cypress, popularly known as 'Macrocarpa'. It is a very fast grower and stands any amount of spray. Given plenty of room to grow when young it stands up to wind very well. Close planting should be resisted, as it runs up very quickly, and if thinned is inclined to blow over. On the west coast of Jersey, a first-class testing ground for seaside trees, it stands up well to the worst of gales. It is not, however, suitable for any but the warmer parts of the British Isles.

Other conifers that thrive by the sea, but, owing to scarcity or high price can only be used as specimens or in small quantities, are Bishop's pine (*P. muricata*), mountain pine (*P. montana*) and stone pine (*P. Pinea*).

Shrubs for Coast Shelterbelts

Shrubs for this purpose must be very hardy, and easily obtainable in quantity. Gardening books often give long lists of shrubs suitable for planting near the sea, but the majority of these are definitely garden species that require shelter. Belt shrubs must be able to do with little shelter, or, better still, with none at all.

For general work in any part of the country two of the best species to use are golden elder and snowberry. They stand up well to ground draught, will grow without much light, and seem quite indifferent to soil. Privet is another useful shrub, whether 'oval-leaved' or common. One of the best blocking shrubs is the much-despised *Aucuba japonica*. It is extremely hardy, and grows under shade better than most shrubs. With its heavily twigged stems and broad leaves it makes a first-class cover against ground draughts.

Other useful shrubs available in quantity are guelder rose and laurustinus. The latter requires some shelter, and, therefore, should not be used on the sea side. *Lonicera nitida* makes good ground cover, and stands up against wind quite well. It is suitable only for the west and south coasts. One of the best shrubs for coast shelter is Sea Buckthorn. It makes a thick bush up to 15 feet in height, grows well in the sandiest of soils, and stand exposure to sea winds better than any other species. Unfortunately it is difficult to obtain in quantity today, but is, however, quite easy to raise from seed.

Tamarisk is one of the most valuable seaside shrubs. This fast-growing species can be used for interplanting trees on the exposed side, and it is specially valuable as a rough hedge 10 to 12 feet in height. It will grow in soil that is almost pure sand, stands spray or wind, and is not affected by occasional floodings at high tide. It is extremely attractive, especially when covered by its masses of pink and white flowers. Tamarisk prefers a warm climate, so is mostly found on the south coast, but quite successful planting has been carried out in Suffolk and as far north as Lincolnshire.

For the use of *Cupressus macrocarpa* as a seaside hedge, see p. 21.

As a semi-formal flowering hedge in the warmer districts, escallonia, especially *E. macrantha*, is strongly recommended. It grows extremely well near the sea, is very decorative and will make a hedge 6 to 8 feet in height. If it is planted on the actual coastline, protection in the shape of wattled hurdles should be provided. When establishing a hedge set the plants 18 inches apart. Pruning should be done after the flowers fade.

Euonymus japonicus, so often commonly used for clipped garden hedges, is largely used for this purpose near the sea, especially on the south coast. It stands strong winds and spray, but requires a certain amount of 'body' in the soil, and is, therefore, not suitable for very sandy soil. The correct interval for planting is 18 inches. It can be clipped with shears twice a year in the same way as other evergreen hedges, and will grow up to 8 feet in height.

As has already been stated, shelter is desirable when establishing seaside screens. Permanent shelter is not essential, but in order to enable young trees and shrubs to establish themselves satisfactorily it should be supplied wherever possible. Even if the barrier is only a few feet high it will make all the difference.

Artificial protection can be provided by using wattled hurdles 5 to 6 feet high. These should not be too closely woven, as it is better for some wind to get through than for it to strike an impenetrable barrier, rise up and crash down on the centre of the planting. For this reason rough hazel hurdles are better than the more expensive types made of willow rods, which are usually very closely plaited together. It is possible today to obtain hurdles made from wide strips of larch. These are cheaper than ordinary wattles, have enough space between the strips to allow for 'wind drift' and last a long time.

Where material is available, a 'brush' fence can be very useful. This consists of heavy, wide-meshed wire fencing 4 to 5 feet high of the type generally known as pig fencing, to which sprays of broom, spruce or pine, or their brushwood are fastened. This combines shelter value with a satisfactory garden fence. Cases occasionally arise of land which, on the seaside, has banks of light or shifting sand, the surface of which is liable in rough weather to blow inland. In such circumstances the site of the garden should be set back, and the sand fixed by covering the area with light brushwood, which can be roughly pegged down. This will decay and help to give body to the sand. The brush should be set with its stem to the wind to prevent 'lifting'. Small Corsican or Austrian pine can then be planted at 5-foot intervals. On flat exposed areas a thin sowing of broom will often help to shelter and force up young trees. If trees are not required tamarisk cuttings might be tried instead. Gorse is occasionally recommended for sowing between young trees to shelter and force them up, but is most undesirable if the adjoining beach is much used by the public, as gorse is highly inflammable.

The width of the screen will depend on the land available for it. As a general rule the wider the screen the better for the garden. In many cases, especially with comparatively small gardens, the belt must be comparatively narrow, but better a thick screen and a small garden than a thin screen and a large garden. The screen should, therefore, be as wide as it can possibly be made. If there is only room for a screen with a few rows of trees, hedges, preferably on both sides, are essential, the outer one being rough and the inner one clipped. In such cases Austrian and Corsican pine with hedges of white poplar (cut hard), thorn or *C. macrocarpa* are suitable. The inside ground filling can be done with aucuba, snowberry and elder.

For very narrow belts in the south, *C. macrocarpa*, reinforced with a hedge or artificial screen, would probably be best. In colder climates Corsican pine might replace *C. macrocarpa*.

Establishment

When making screen belts near the sea, trees must be planted in soil that has been well dug over. Clay soils should be trenched two spits deep, and chalks dug over, at the same time breaking up the subsoil and, if the soil layer is thin, the chalk immediately below. The best soil must in all cases be kept on top, where it is available for rooting purposes.

Trees should be set 4 feet apart. If they are planted at wider intervals height growth is comparatively slow, and the trees tend to spread out and so lose height. Set at the interval recommended, the trees are forced up rapidly and can be thinned out—in fact, *must* be thinned out—as soon as the lower branches touch, otherwise these branches, if left to themselves, will die off, and valuable shelter will be lost.

As in all cases of planting, the trees used should be stocky and well-rooted, and if evergreens, small. Large evergreens are difficult to move at any time, and near the sea they are even more so. When sea-coast planting is being done it does not pay to be impatient.

27. *Tamarisk on the sea front at Bognor Regis.*

28. Damage that can be caused to gardens, drains and building foundations by poplar roots.

CHAPTER IX

HEDGES, TREES AND THE LAW

THE landowner who plants hedges or trees on the boundaries of his property must accept certain responsibilities for such action. From the legal point of view he must not allow his planting to become a 'nuisance' to his neighbours or to the general public. This, in law, may be defined as something that may cause injury, damage or inconvenience to others. Injury and damage are usually matters of fact, but inconvenience is not always easy to prove, and in some cases there is no legal remedy for it. Apart from legal responsibility the 'good neighbour' policy should not be forgotten. Too often people are apt to forget that members of a community have a moral duty to one another in avoiding irritation or annoyance leading to anger, and too often this is caused by selfishness or neglect rather than by ignorance.

Liability to Fence

The ownership of land does not include any obligation to fence or plant hedges. The owner is, therefore, not liable for any damage caused to cattle, belonging to another person, that may enter on his land. Should these cattle, however, do damage on or to the land their owner will be liable. No man, in fact, need fence against another man's cattle.

Boundary Hedges

It may be presumed that, provided there is no evidence to the contrary, the ownership of land on which a hedge stands with a boundary ditch on its outer side, extends to the far edge of the ditch. It is presumed that when making the ditch the owner excavated it on the edge of his property, throwing the earth back on to his land, and planting the hedge on the mound or ridge thus formed.

If the hedge has a ditch on both sides, or on neither side, in the absence of documentary evidence of ownership the only way to

G

settle the question is by proving acts of ownership, i.e. ditching, cutting and laying, replanting or trimming, or felling and removing trees. In such cases it seems necessary to prove that the adjacent owner knew of or acquiesced in these acts and raised no objection to them.

If a ditch exists, but has been so damaged or neglected that the exact edge cannot be determined, the distance from the hedge can sometimes be settled by reference to local custom, the usual width allowed being about 4 to 6 feet from the root of the hedge. A court of law is, however, not necessarily bound by 'custom of the country'. If no ditch exists and there is no evidence that a ditch ever existed it has been held by the House of Lords[1] that the previous existence of a ditch cannot be presumed and a 4-foot margin claimed for it.

A point in connection with boundary hedges which may arise is one where land is sold, and the boundary is based on field edges indicated by lines on the Ordnance Survey, lines which invariably indicate the centre of the hedge rather than the boundary as it may appear to the intending purchaser. With the increase in the use of agricultural land for housing purposes this problem is likely to arise more frequently. Ownership in common of a hedge is likely to produce difficult and exasperating problems, especially where a keen gardener tends his half of the hedge very carefully only to find his efforts frustrated by a neighbour who refuses to do anything to his side. The solution is obviously to make very certain before purchasing the land not only what the boundary is, but where it is, though in practice this may be difficult.

Overgrowing Branches

If branches from a hedge extend over another person's land the owner of the land has certain remedies. He can lop the branches back to his boundary, but before doing so must give the hedge-owner notice of his proposed action, in order to give him the opportunity of doing the work himself if he so wishes. The loppings remain the property of the hedge-owner, and may not be utilized in any way by the landowner who has cut them. But if he is in a position to prove damage he can take action against

[1]See *Law Times*, May 8, 1920.   (Collis *v.* Amphlett.)

the hedge-owner. A landowner has a perfect right to cut away hedge roots that may be trespassing on his land. This is an important point where small gardens are concerned. A big privet hedge, for example, may extend its roots for yards, and being a very hungry feeder may utterly ruin a considerable portion of such gardens.

Trees in Hedges: Possibility of Damage

As the law stands at present an owner does not appear to be liable for accidents caused by falling trees unless he knew or ought to have known that the tree which fell was dangerous. There is a point not generally grasped in connection with hedgerow trees that applies particularly to the potential danger of trees which are naturally shallow-rooted, the best example being elm. Most old hedges, especially those on roadsides, have a ditch on one side or the other. When the roots of an elm reach the ditch, especially a deep, well-kept one, they do not go downwards to any extent, but tend to run sideways along the bank. This produces a weak lopsided root system, and the taller the tree grows the more likely it is to fall at any time. The same trouble in an even more aggravated form is likely to occur with elm and ash, in fact, almost any tree grown in a hedge at the top of a high bank which, in the case of a sunken road, may be almost vertical. In such cases the main roots may run down the bank just below, or even showing above, the surface, and the tree is largely kept erect by the roots on the field side. Such trees blow down very easily, and a tree-owner in such circumstances may find it very difficult to prove that there was no reason why he should have known that the tree was dangerous.

Branches, of course, can get into a dangerous condition without interfering with the stability of the tree, and these can be dealt with by lopping. This can be done by an adjoining landowner, after giving notice, but he cannot recover the cost of lopping from the tree-owner, although he might bring an action for trespass, basing the damages on the lopping cost. Alternatively he can warn the tree-owner that in his opinion the tree, or certain branches, are dangerous, and leave him to take action. If the tree-owner takes no action, either by carrying out the work or by obtaining expert opinion on the tree, his position, should an accident occur, is not a very sound one.

The Barbed Wire Act

An idea appears to be prevalent that the use of barbed wire within 6 feet of a highway is illegal. This is not exactly correct. Barbed wire can apparently be used close to any public path or road irrespective of distance, provided that the Local Authority does not consider it dangerous. If, on the other hand, the Authority considers it to be a nuisance (which amounts to it being dangerous) notice can be served ordering it to be removed from the dangerous position. The time given to carry out the work is generally one month, and never more than six months. If the work is not done the Authority can obtain an Order to do the work itself, and charge the owner with the cost. The legal definition of barbed wire appears to be any wire with jagged spikes or projections.

Dangerous Hedges

It would appear that anyone owning a hedge which, by reason of its condition, causes damage or injury is liable to have an action brought against him. There is, for example, the instance where a child climbing into a defective hedge won his case.

For this reason owners of garden hedges protected on the road side by wattled hurdles, a widespread practice today, should satisfy themselves by frequent inspection that they are in a satisfactory condition, and not likely to injure passers-by. The split shoots that form the main part of wattle hurdling are held in place by being forced behind the uprights, and are at all times in a state of tension. Should one end work out from the stake which holds it in, it is liable to project from the hurdle in such a way that anyone running along the path at dusk or in darkness might meet with very serious injury.

Obstruction by Hedges

Under Section 23 of the Public Health Act 1925, the Local Authority has the power to order the removal or cutting back of any tree, hedge or shrub that is considered to be obstructing the view of direction signs set up by County Councils, from road users, whether drivers of vehicles or pedestrians, or, in the case of a street lamp, to be obstructing the light. If the owner fails to carry out the specified work within the given time (generally fourteen days) the Local Authority may do the work and recover the costs from the owner.

Damage to Hedges Caused by Hunting

In the ordinary way, if hedges or fences are damaged by the Hunt, the Hunt is apparently responsible for making good the damage (usually paid for out of the 'wire fund' raised for this purpose). Present-day agricultural practice has, however, produced a new problem in the T.T. herd, and the consequent damage that may result from such cattle getting out, or other cattle getting in, through newly-made gaps, and this no doubt will eventually be decided by the Courts.

Poisonous Plants

There are certain trees or shrubs with poisonous leaves or fruits which, in certain circumstances, should not be used for hedge planting. The outstanding species is yew, the foliage of which usually has a fatal effect on cattle that may happen to eat it. For this reason yew should never be used for a garden hedge adjoining grazing land, unless it stands well away from the boundary or is so fenced that animals cannot get at it.

A farmer appears to have no claim against a hedge-owner if his animals have eaten yew foliage that is growing inside the hedge boundary. But if, on the other hand, the animals eat foliage from branches that were projecting over the boundary line into the field, or hedge clippings that had been thrown into the field, the position would be very different.

Animals have been known to eat yew foliage without ill effect, but in many cases they have become seriously ill, or have died. It seems also that half-withered foliage has been found to have greater toxic properties than foliage in full growth, so that clippings or foliage or cut branch sprays should always be carefully collected and removed.

Yew arils, or berries, are attractive to young children, owing to their bright colour and peculiar shape, and at least one child has died after eating them. The toxic property is, however, confined to the kernel, as children have been known to eat the pulp without ill effect. It does not necessarily follow that because a yew hedge is clipped no berries will ever be found on it.

Box and Cherry Laurel

Although not common there are cases where cattle have been poisoned by eating the leaves of these species.

Daphne Mezereum

Occasionally found as a hedge plant. The berries are bright scarlet, rather resembling currants. They contain an irritant poison, which has caused illness and even death when the berries have been eaten in large quantities.

Sea Buckthorn

Bird lovers should avoid planting this tree in quantity. The berries have an acrid taste, and are for this reason usually avoided, but there have recently been cases of death where these berries have been eaten by birds.

Apart from any legal action which may follow poisoning by hedge plants, the planting or harbouring of plants of this kind should be avoided in places where the berries or seeds may be eaten by the ignorant or the very young. With large numbers of hedge-making species to choose from there is no need to be anti-social.

Damage by Roots to Houses

An important point for the consideration of owners contemplating the planting of hedges and screens, especially the latter, is the possibility of damage to adjoining buildings. If trees and shrubs are planted on or near a boundary it is only to be expected that their roots will spread outwards, and in doing so penetrate the soil belonging to the adjoining owner. As they grow the trees drop twigs and leaves which fill up gutters, and branches swinging in the wind may damage roofs. Roots, especially of those which have a shallow-growing habit, may interfere with garden cultivation and impoverish the soil. They may also do damage by lifting paving, and even cracking walls, by the force exerted as they grow. Moisture-loving trees such as poplars can do considerable damage to drainage systems in their search for water, as their fibres, penetrating even the smallest crack in a joint, can completely block a pipe.

An actual example typical of the damage that poplars can do may be of interest. A row of black poplars stood on the boundary of an estate, with a high board fence within a few feet. This separated the trees from a garage and cottage standing on adjacent property, the nearest wall of the garage being some 20 feet from the trees, which were about fifty years old. The buildings were approximately the same age. Complaint was made that the concrete 'washdown' of the garage was cracking, and that there was increasing difficulty in opening the heavy garage doors, the hangings and posts of which appeared to be in perfect order. Water refused to run away from the sump in the centre of the 'washdown'. As the concrete was obviously 'lifting', root damage was suspected, and examination showed this suspicion to be well grounded. Sections of the concrete were taken up, and pressed against them several roots were found; in one case the root was 8 inches in diameter. The sump was full of root fibre, which had forced itself through the joints. When this was removed the sump still refused to empty, and further examination showed that the escape pipe had been lifted to such an extent that the end of the affected pipe was higher than the level of the sump escape hole. Cases such as this are far from uncommon. Poplars are the worst offenders, but ash and elm are well-known offenders as far as the blocking of drainage pipes is concerned. The fact that cases of drain blocking seem more numerous than they used to be is possibly due to the vast increase of comparatively cheap houses, where drain-joints have been sealed with inferior material, or possibly not sealed at all.

From the legal point of view it would appear that the encroachment of roots from a neighbour's tree is much the same thing as a branch which overhangs another's land. If the offending root is merely growing in the soil the only remedy open to the soil-owner is to cut it off, and this he has every right to do. If, on the other hand, the root is blocking a pipe, pushing up paving stones, or in fact doing any damage that causes expense, it constitutes a 'nuisance', and the person whose property has been, or is being, damaged can not only abate the nuisance by removing or destroying the roots, but can bring an action for damages against the owner of the tree.

In practice, if the trees are not standing on or very close to the boundary it is not always easy to identify the actual tree to which the root belongs, but there seems little doubt that if a root can be traced up to the boundary this should be enough for all practical, and even legal, purposes.

Other entrances to pipes now available to roots are the cracks and open joints caused by bomb damage. There must be many thousands of such pipes still functioning more or less efficiently as water carriers, but which may easily get choked if moisture-loving trees are planted in the vicinity.

Roots of poplars, indeed roots of all trees, growing under garden walls or wooden fences may cause tilting of considerable lengths of wall or fence, and this is especially so when trees are standing close up to the boundary. As has already been stated, the owner of the affected land is entitled to cut away roots extending from adjacent property, but he must not forget that this action will only bring temporary relief, for as long as the trees stand the root ends will shoot in the same way as a cut branch. If he finds his drains full of tree roots, and can identify the source, he should have a good case for legal remedy against the owner. The trees that give most trouble as a rule are naturally shallow-rooted. Oak, chestnut and other deep-rooting trees seldom give trouble. Complaints about conifers appear to be comparatively rare.

Another type of mechanical damage may be caused by the actual expansion of the tree trunk, or the root buttresses at soil-level. This may affect boundary walls and wooden fences sited close to the tree. Brick and other walls may be pushed out of true, or cracked by the growing tree pressing against the masonry. Root buttresses will lift and crack masonry, and force wooden pale fences upwards and out of line. The sway of a tree may also cause damage by root movement. In some of these cases the wall-owner cannot take direct action, as he may not go on to the tree-owner's land, but if he thinks he can prove that the damage is being done by the tree, and its owner refuses to do anything about it, he would be perfectly justified in taking legal proceedings.

There is also a possibility of damage to buildings by settlement, caused by loss of soil moisture due to the root action of trees which have been planted close by.

Such damage appears to be mainly confined to buildings with comparatively shallow foundations standing in heavy clay soils, soils which are liable to considerable shrinkage, especially in dry weather. Shrinkage being due to loss of soil moisture, it is not difficult to imagine the result when, to the normal loss of moisture, are added the demands of fast-growing trees that need large quantities of water in order to live. No accurate figures exist regarding the actual amount of water required by various species, but it is well known that poplar, a species very commonly planted near houses, requires a great deal of water—probably far more than most other species. Growing in clay soils, where lateral movement of water is extremely slow, the roots will extend to great distances in search of moisture, and cases have been reported where suckers from the roots of trees planted on one side of a house have been seen growing on the far side. Roots ramify when in search of moisture and throw out masses of fibre, which may extend right through the upper sub-soil below a building. The degree of moisture extraction and root spread depends upon the species of tree, and poplar appears to be the worst offender.

When a shrinkable soil loses water its volume decreases in proportion to the water lost. It cracks and settles. In south-east England, where most of the damage to buildings seems to occur, there is generally enough rain in winter to saturate the soil. In summer, however, evaporation tends to exceed rainfall, so that moisture deficiency develops. It has been generally believed in the past that water rises from the sub-soil to replace what is removed, but recent research shows that this is not so.

Owing to root action moisture deficiency is always greater where vegetable growth exists. If, during the summer, water is drawn by roots from a soil already deficient in moisture the degree of deficiency must be greatly increased. And if these roots are growing under a house, the shelter of which prevents the soil from getting its fair share of rain, a permanent moisture deficiency is liable to be set up.

A simple example showing how poplar tree roots may affect the soil moisture content can be given. The figures are not exact as regards actual moisture requirement, as no such figures are yet available, but they are sufficient for the purpose in hand. It is suggested by reliable experts on the subject that an established fruit tree might use somewhere about 4,500 gallons of water per annum. If a fruit tree needs this amount a poplar certainly will use this amount, and probably a great deal more; say, 6,000 gallons. In a dry season the annual rainfall may not exceed 22 inches, of which 11 inches may be disposed of by evaporation. In such a case the result of tree planting might be as follows:

Three poplars growing near a small house have a root system, one side of which has penetrated below the house, affecting an area on that side of, say, 30 feet by 30 feet, i.e. 100 square yards, or 1/48th of an acre. With a 22-inch rainfall the loss of moisture by evaporation, etc., is possibly 11 inches, leaving 11 inches in the soil. On 1/48th of an acre this is equivalent to about 5,000 gallons of water. If we now take the figure of 6,000 gallons as the requirement per tree (a figure very much less than that suggested by experts on the subject) then the three trees would require about 18,000 gallons per annum between them, half of which should be obtained by the root system on the house side; all the soil water and more, in fact[1].

From this it can be realized that the presence of poplar roots can result in a very considerable loss of volume, i.e. shrinkage, which in its turn is liable to produce cracking and settlement of buildings.

The figures in this example must not be taken literally. They do, however, present a very fair picture of the situation that may arise when trees in a clay soil are planted close to houses.

It might be argued that houses on clay are damaged by settlement in places where no trees exist, but, on the other hand, wide-

[1] Water will, of course, work in from undepleted areas, but owing to soil friction its progress is usually extremely slow, too slow, in fact, to prevent soil movements in the 'dried out' section.

spread investigation shows that while there are many houses on clay that are apparently undamaged there are very few houses to be found with poplars growing close to them that do not show damage of some kind. Ward[1] states that after constant search he has 'yet to find a traditional brick house founded on shrinkable clay in the south-east of England, with a row of poplar trees about fifteen or more years old, planted since the house was constructed, parallel to and 20 feet or closer to one side of the building, where visible movement and cracking has not occurred during the periods 1942–45 and 1947'.

And again, it is possible to find a house badly damaged by settlement, that house being the only one in the road that shows signs of damage, and the only one with poplar trees growing near it.

From the legal point of view the fact that damage to buildings can be caused by the abnormal extraction of soil moisture by roots appears to have been accepted by the Courts, rulings having been given to the effect that if the roots of a tree belonging to an adjoining owner had trespassed into the property of another person, and in doing so had caused damage by absorbing water and weakening foundations, there was legitimate cause for action against the tree-owner.

If trees are to be felled to avoid possibility of damage, or to prevent further damage occurring, destruction must be very thorough. Felling the trees is not enough, as they will shoot again, and so keep the roots alive. If the stump cannot be taken out it should be thoroughly barked with a sharp spade, or a fire can be lighted over it. Roots should be severed near the stump if possible. If suckers appear they should be cut away, and a short length of the root to which they are attached should be dug down to, and cut away. One of the best means for killing a stump outright is to soak it with petrol and set it alight.

It appears, therefore, that to plant forest trees, and especially fast-growing varieties such as poplar or willow, in clay soil close to houses, the foundations of which are less than 3 feet in depth, may lead to considerable trouble and expense. Whether or not

---

[1] W. H. Ward: 'The Effect of Vegetation on the Settlement of Structures'. *Proc. Conf. Biology and Civil Eng*. Institute of Civil Engineers. 1948.

these trees will cause damage depends a good deal on the species. Laterally-rooting trees, such as elms and poplars, frequently develop a root equal to, or even exceeding, the actual height of the tree. Tap-rooting trees such as oak may produce long laterals, but the main body of roots is generally close to the tree, and fairly deep in the soil. If damage by roots is to be avoided the obvious thing to do is to plant trees at such a distance that the roots can do no harm. With poplars this is at least 75 feet. Generally speaking the smaller the habit of the tree the smaller is the root system, and, aesthetically, small trees are far more suitable for small gardens and houses than large trees.

INDEX